D1286245

The Entrepreneur

VOLUME ONE

The Last Days in Monaco

HANS SITTER

KING'S PUBLISHING

The Entrepreneur: Volume One: The Last Days in Monaco

©Copyright 2015 by Hans Sitter

All rights reserved.

No part of this book may be reproduced in any written, electronic, recording, or photocopying without written permission of the publisher or author. The exception would be in the case of quotations for critical articles or reviews where permission is specifically granted by the publisher or author.

Although every precaution has been taken to verify the accuracy of the information contained herein, the author and publisher assume no responsibility for any errors or omissions. No liability is assumed for damages that may result from the use of information contained within.

Books may be purchased by contacting the publisher and author at:
info@kingsbiergarten.com

Published by

King's Publishing
1329 East Broadway St., Pearland, TX 77581

Cover and Interior Design: Nick Zelinger, NZ Graphics
Editor: John Maling (Editing By John)
Manuscript Consultant: Judith Briles (The Book Shepherd)

Library of Congress Cataloging in Publication Data
ISBN: 978-0-9862427-0-0 (Hard Cover)
ISBN: 978-0-9862427-1-7 (Soft Cover)
ISBN: 978-0-9862427-2-4 (eBook)

Monday, Monday
Words and Music by John Phillips
Copyright © 1966 UNIVERSAL MUSIC CORP.
Copyright Renewed
All Rights Reserved Used by Permission
Reprinted by Permission of Hal Leonard Corporation

1) Business   2) Entrepreneur   3) Memoir

First Edition Printed in Canada

To Tony Robbins, my son, Philipp
and my beautiful wife, Megan

Dear Marilyn

I hope you enjoy my
book and I wish you
the best.

10-8-16

1

Thursday in April 1996

*My three-million-dollar deal and its promise of total
liberation and a new beginning seemed awfully solid.*

People talk about their hearts pounding—their hearts pounding
so loud that they can practically hear them. What about the
brain? Can it pound like an errant heart, with audible wave after
wave of pain crashing on the shore of consciousness, until the
owner wants to scream?

For me, the answer was a resounding yes. Whether or not this
type of pain is possible for others, I can swear to you that it is an
unadorned description of what I experienced as I walked down
the pier towards my yacht. The *Macau* was safely moored in
Fontvieille, one of Monte Carlo's ports. The *Macau* was my
home, a place I associated with sanctuary and rest. I named her
after the former Portuguese colony sometimes known as the
Monte Carlo of the Orient, now ceded to the Chinese but still a
Mecca for gamblers from all over the world.

Monte Carlo was to be my pay day. I had only been back a few days, but I was expecting money—a great deal of money. It had been scheduled to come already but had not arrived, so I began to worry—big-time worry. I loved Monte Carlo, but with my head pounding away, I was seeing my favorite city through a distorted lens of pain.

Yes, I was back in Monaco with my beautiful blonde wife, Karin, a fun-loving but complex companion, and Philipp, my two-and-a-half-year-old son. If I felt ambivalent about my wife nowadays, there were no such feelings about Philipp whom I loved conditionally. Philipp was the sweetest little kid you could imagine—friendly, always with a big smile on his face. He was blond with grey-green eyes, like his mother but there was no confusion or turbulence in them, unlike Karin's eyes—just the purity of a happy child.

Trotting somewhere behind me was another official member of my little family, Umberto. Umberto was my little Cavalier King Charles Spaniel. He was my pet, my friend and bodyguard, and went everywhere with me. I don't remember the last time I took him out with a leash, but now he somehow sensed the dark cloud that surrounded me and kept his distance.

Generally when I took a walk, it was never alone; Philipp and Umberto were on each side. We attracted a lot of attention. We were just plain cute, my little son bobbing along on one side of me and the little dog trotting along with us. Umberto, despite his gender, looked a lot like Lady from the Disney movie *Lady and the Tramp*, with those long, floppy ears and big brown eyes. Neither one of them was with me at the moment, and I felt quite alone, suffering from the "grandfather of all headaches," trying to comfort myself with a kind of relentless cross-examination—

why was everything so terrible? Why? Nobody had died. Nobody was in the hospital. This was just about financial pain. It wasn't supposed to be.

This was the worst kind of pain for someone like me, an inveterate entrepreneur. Financial pain is always a danger signal, a red light flashing in the survival center of the brain telling you that you could lose everything you worked for, dreamed of and loved. It's pain that we serial entrepreneurs know all too well. Physical pain is bad, but fiscal pain is definitely something to be reckoned with too. And when you love Monte Carlo as much as I do, you don't want to associate it with pain of any sort.

MONACO

"There is no income tax."

Monaco is the country where the fabulous city of Monte Carlo is found. For most, Monaco connotes an annual *Formula One* racing event in the spring; the Monte Carlo *Rolex Masters*, a major tennis tournament in the fall; and of course Monaco's most famous attraction, Le Casino de Monte-Carlo.

Oh, of course, there also is the still widely-remembered marriage of Prince Rainier with the legendary American actress, Grace Kelly, in the fifties. That made a powerful impression on the world, infusing people's thoughts of Monaco with a fairytale quality even now, more than a half a century later.

Monaco is actually a small sovereign state, a state on the north-central coast, nestled on the beautiful Mediterranean between France and Italy. It is composed of several key regions—Monte Carlo with Le Casino de Monte-Carlo and the Hotel de Paris in the center, Monaco Ville, La Condamine, Fontvieille and

Larvotto Beach. Although it has a huge international reputation, Monaco's actual size is less than two square miles, with an estimated population of around 33,000. An average person can walk across the width of the country in an hour. The original citizens of Monaco are called Monagasques. They are not rich, but Monaco has a very broad social net. For them, everything is free—kindergarten, schools, universities, health insurance. Most Monagasques are members of the working class or have shops, restaurants or other types of small businesses. There is no income tax.

Interestingly, Monagasques are not allowed in the casino, a fact that no doubt helps protect their modest but comfortable income and lifestyle. Of the town's 33,000 or so inhabitants, only about 7,600 are Monagasques. Of the remaining 27,400, most are foreigners, consisting of 125 different nationalities—many of them quite wealthy. In order to qualify for permanent residency, they had to possess, as I did, a *Carte de Sejour*, roughly equivalent to a Green Card in the United States.

> IT'S A TINY COUNTRY— MONACO'S ACTUAL SIZE IS LESS THAN TWO SQUARE MILES, WITH AN ESTIMATED POPULATION OF AROUND 33,000. AN AVERAGE PERSON CAN WALK ACROSS THE WIDTH OF THE COUNTRY IN AN HOUR.

The *Carte de Sejour* comes at a high price. For one thing, you have to prove you have some kind of permanent residence in Monaco, a house or an apartment, and that you live in Monaco at least six months a year. Back then, I had bought a fully-furnished apartment for $100,000 with the lease contract included in the purchase, plus about $10,000 for all the related fees and legal advice.

Any foreigner who manages to live in Monaco on a permanent basis is quite lucky because Monaco is a tax haven, a state that does not collect income tax from its citizens or its permanent residents. Despite its other charms, this is the main reason why I and many other foreigners were residents. Imagine that—no income taxes!

We entrepreneurs consider that a dream come true. The fact is most inhabitants could probably afford to pay taxes, but that is not the custom of the super-rich, who try to hang on to every cent. That's what quite a few of these foreigners are, of course: movie stars, European and Middle Eastern royalty, lots of famous tennis players and Formula One race car drivers. If you love exotic, expensive cars like Ferraris, Lamborghinis, Rolls Royces and Bentleys, then you should come here. I promise you that you will never see more exotic, luxurious cars being driven or parked so close together.

3

The Deal—Trouble?

Three million sounds like a lot of money ...

Umberto now caught up with me, trotting happily beside me as we walked through a fantastic gauntlet of 50- to 150-foot yachts owned by some of the richest people in the world. I really loved mine, and I was very proud to get a slip. To me, this was where real wealth was, owning something like my little yacht.

My head still ached as I approached my slip and climbed gratefully into my 47-footer. As I stepped on the deck, I thought: *Maybe if I could just sit down for a few minutes and relax, I could think clearly.* When that didn't work, I did some push-ups and sit-ups. I felt as if worry had squeezed all the oxygen out my bloodstream. And when that didn't work, I tried some stretching and yoga. At some point, as I coiled my body upwards in the cobra position, staring at a point in the sky, a little wave of relaxation swept over me, and I felt myself sighing as the pounding receded.

I also think that just being near those grand boats surrounding the *Macau* made me feel better.

At last I could reflect for a moment. I went over to a deck chair, sat down, and began to lecture myself quite sternly.

Johann Sitter, you are in one of the most wonderful places in the world, so shut up—and relax. Look at the waves pounding on the surf, licking at the foot of the pier. Sit down in your damn 47-foot yacht, which you still own, and try to think of all the good things in your life. Feel the sun, breathe the air, for Christ's sake.

Okay, maybe I should give myself a little bit of a break, I thought, reminding myself that, after all, the circumstances were a bit unusual.

For the last few weeks you were loafing a bit, waiting for the inevitable wire transfer of three million dollars to your favorite little bank in Monte Carlo. Three million bucks— that ought to make you rest easy. It ought to be enough to carry you over to a new life and career in the U.S.

My three-million-dollar deal and its promise of total liberation and a new beginning seemed awfully solid, except to the back of my head where the pain was unrelenting.

Three million sounds like a lot of money, but in Monaco I would say it was not much of an asset. Still, it was enough to comfortably finance that longed-for move to the New World. It was 1996. I was going to be 43-years-old in a week, and I was looking forward to getting away from our anti-entrepreneurial, so-called socialist democracy in Austria, where my businesses were located. Don't misunderstand—I love Austria. It's a gorgeous country, and the people who live there are hardworking and friendly, but unfortunately, like every mostly socialist country, it's very hard to make money there. Of course, I would always want to visit Austria. We have an amazingly rich culture; our cities are fabulous, filled with history. No other country has been the birthplace of so many great composers—Mozart, Haydn, Bach, Strauss—and so many more.

Yes, Austria is a great country, but not for my kind of business: trading, dealing, flipping properties, creating an idea and selling a concept. The taxes are far too high and the rules too complicated for anyone to do these things freely and fluidly. And, Austria was definitely not business friendly.

I needed to move out of Austria so that I could pursue these types of enterprises. One of the greatest things I had ever created was a fitness center called *Freizeittempel*, architecturally inspired by a trip to Caesar's Palace in Las Vegas where I had married Karin, my second wife.

Roughly translated "The Temple of Leisure," this luxurious fitness center with its golden dome and massive Greek columns was part of a complex that contained a 20-room hotel and a fine-dining Italian restaurant called *La Ponte* (The Bridge), as well as five indoor courts for badminton and squash. The price I got was $3,000,000.

My hotel may have had only 20 rooms, but every room was exquisite, built in the style of the fitness center, which offered a serious retreat for rebuilding and conditioning the body combined with a splash of pampering and luxury. Classically severe, Roman-looking rooms contrasted with the exotic paintings I chose to decorate them, and the rigors of weightlifting and aerobics were tempered by a gorgeous wet area with sauna, whirlpools, steam rooms and tanning beds, laced with exotic palm trees. The crowning touch: a beautiful fitness bar done in polished wood that served tempting fresh-fruit smoothies.

This expensive-looking tourist center had certainly caught the attention of the 45,000 inhabitants of Wiener Neustadt (Vienna New Town), which was located in lower Austria, about 30 miles south of Vienna, my home town. Now after four years of losses on the project, I knew I had to dump my little Leisure Temple and hotel complex—but where and on whom?

During this time, Karin really enjoyed the *Freizeittempel*. Any time she used the facility, she was treated like royalty by our employees, who looked up to her, as did the whole town of Wiener Neustadt. When she visited a hair salon or nail studio, "Mrs. Sitter" was always someone to be greeted by her last name, fawned on, protected and complimented. She enjoyed being *someone* in our little city—too much to care whether I lost money or made money with our great little gymnasium complex. The only thing that counted for her was that everyone admired her, thought she was rich and gave her more attention than she deserved.

Despite its problems, I still believed in the *Freizeittempel*—I just didn't believe in my ability to maintain it or my interest in doing so. I never thought of "dumping" it on someone because it was intrinsically worthless. I thought of "dumping" it because of my lack of patience with maintenance tasks and my hope was the new owner would know how to take care of it and promote it.

I JUST DIDN'T BELIEVE IN MY ABILITY TO MAINTAIN IT OR MY INTEREST IN DOING SO.

Ultimately, all my hopes came to rest with a man named Linkov, a truly strange character on whom I suppose I projected entrepreneurial powers that would make the gym hum with financial energy and make him a mint, while rescuing me and my family from a financial black hole that was rapidly consuming my entire universe.

Herr Linkov

*He didn't bat an eye, but said immediately,
"I'll give you three million and not one dime more.
Say 'yes' and we have a deal."*

Besides *Freizeittempel,* I had another property, a huge nightclub that had cost me two million dollars to build. I called it The Beverly Hills Club, and by the time I met Linkov, it had been open for six months. The club was spectacular, boasting a huge neon wall in front, flickering with a powerful Las Vegas ambiance. I got a great deal of recognition for this project too. It was a men's club with table dancing, loaded with absolutely the latest in dance-floor technology.

I got the idea from my friend Fritz Titzer, who had gone to the U.S. for vacation. He had visited a men's club of this type in Miami and decided to bring the concept to Vienna, where he built the pilot project in the First District, around the corner from a Marriott Hotel. Rather than simply clone the original idea, Fritz adapted it to suit the local culture in Vienna. The Beverly Hills Club was a place for the discerning guest, a place to relax and experience the magic of gorgeous dancers moving to hot rhythms and a great light show.

Fritz often visited *Freizeittempel*, and when I went to Vienna I often visited him at his club. He convinced me to build one in Wiener Neustadt, and I did. I would put up the money, he'd run it and we would split the profits. I know now that this was a big mistake. The Beverly Hills Club was too much and too big for Wiener Neustadt. I didn't understand that when we opened— bigness was the whole idea. And bigness just wasn't Wiener Neustadt.

At the grand opening an airplane passed overhead, releasing twenty skydivers who floated down in front of the entrance. Promptly at 8:00 p.m. we began a massive fireworks display, hitherto unheard of in Wiener Neustadt, with hundreds of people on the streets watching the spectacle. During the first couple of weeks, we were packed every day.

But then the City got involved. One day sobriety checkpoints began to pop up on every street surrounding the club. Any time someone left, they were sure to be stopped and forced to take a breath test. A lot of my clients actually wound up spending the night in jail and being prosecuted for drunk driving. Three or four months later, the business was just about gone. My beautiful little town had done its best to kill my investment.

Before this happened, in what appeared to be a fortuitous event, a Herr Linkov showed up at the club. He spent money like crazy, particularly on the girls, who showered him with attention. He would always have three or four girls at his table, and each one would get paid a couple of hundred dollars for her trouble. He was behaving exactly like a multi-millionaire.

Fascinated, I decided to introduce myself. When he learned I was the owner, he got very excited and ordered champagne for me and the girls. By the time his visit to the club was over, he had rung up a bill for $5,400. I will never forget it. His behavior intrigued me, so I invited him to join me for dinner the next day in my restaurant at the *Freizeittempel*.

He accepted my invitation and came with his wife. Her name was Barbara. He boasted that she was 30 years younger than he was and how funny it was when people first met her. "The idiots," he laughed out loud, "they think she is my daughter. Then they tell me how pretty my daughter is. Every time!" he continued, thinking this was hilarious. When I sized him up, I saw that here was a man who really lived to show off his wealth, and possibly his power, to everyone around him, whatever the cost.

To be like this, I knew he had to have a big problem with himself, and when I looked at him, I understood why. Something psychologists might call low self-esteem—maybe because, basically, Linkov was short, fat and ugly, and he compensated for his negative perception of himself by being flamboyant with his clothes, cash and attractive young wife.

Before too long—and, admittedly, understanding something of his character—I came to believe that he would enjoy owning something like my local enterprises—there'd be plenty of opportunities to show off. So I broached the idea of selling him the hotel and the club.

I didn't have to try very hard. As soon as I dangled the bait, he bit hard. His eyes widened noticeably, and he became immediately interested and engaged. When I showed him my apartment, the hotel rooms and the gym, his enthusiasm grew. And when we returned to the restaurant after the presentation, his only question was, "How much?"

I told him about the bank loan he would have to take over, but all he came back with was, "How much cash?"

First I said, "Five million."

He didn't bat an eye, but said immediately, "I'll give you three million and not one dime more. Say 'yes' and we have a deal."

How I could possibly imagine that Linkov was even somewhat real is now beyond me. The handwriting was on the wall, but I didn't want to see it. Linkov was a man who wrote himself very large—so large that nobody could really understand what he was talking about. He told me he was a broker, but I wasn't quite sure of what he actually sold. He was like the derivative brokers featured in the movie Matt Damon produced, *Inside Job*. Anytime he talked about what he brokered, people would look puzzled or go to sleep.

Whatever Linkov was selling, it was clearly not derivatives, but some other even more abstruse category of stocks and bonds. Still, while he was talking and his listeners were trying to assess what he was saying, how could they not notice his exquisitely tailored silk shirts and tie, and that big, fat, gold chain around his neck? How could they help but notice how well he tipped?

WHO CARES ABOUT THE COLOR OF ROBIN HOOD'S DOUBLET, AS LONG AS IT'S A DARK, VIBRANT GREEN?

I suppose I was like the average Linkov watcher. To me he seemed to emanate big money, very big money, even though what he was doing always eluded me. I wasn't sure whether he was a financial genius or a complete moron. It didn't cross my mind that he was a con. Lack of clarity is a warning signal. I should have noticed it back then, but Linkov's flamboyant mannerisms were so unusual, I couldn't place him in any familiar category. Besides, sometimes the eagerness to do a deal can be blinding.

In my case, I really wanted to get rid of everything that tied me to Wiener Neustadt as fast as possible. I had my blindfolds on. I had had enough and took a chance at rolling the dice at the casino called "Linkov." So, like a few others who dabble in deals of this magnitude, I chose to believe in his financial genius. Linkov became, in my eyes, the Robin Hood who would rescue me and give me back my financial freedom. And even though I couldn't understand a word he said, I figured it was just the higher plane of financial reality that he inhabited. Who cares about the color of Robin Hood's doublet, as long as it's a dark, vibrant green?

Linkov said he was doing millions of dollars of business with brokers in America. I initially thought that was a stretch, but when I went over to his house to sign the contract, we went in through a side door—and passed through a garage that housed some very impressive cars: a Viper, a Rolls Royce, a Ferrari, a Porsche and a few others that even I could not identify, but they looked damned expensive. The house was huge, with a swimming pool. The open living room alone, with its various levels, was at least 10,000 square feet. So despite my skepticism, I bought into the idea that he was rich, probably well-connected too, and the ideal person to take over my palatial gymnasium, hotel and amenities—and the Beverly Hills Club.

After signing the contract, we trucked over to the bank. There I was treated to absolute proof that this dandified stranger had $20 million in his account. Sitting at a banker's desk, we finalized certain other elements of the deal—the hotel complex itself and my gorgeous apartment on the second floor. We made a separate contract for the Beverly Hills Club.

To complete the transaction, Herr Linkov had to take over my bank loan and provide me with $3 million in cash, which would be my real profit on the deal. I insisted, of course, that the money be transferred directly to an account in Monaco so I could legally avoid the mammoth taxes that would be levied by the State of Austria. Linkov also signed a binding agreement making the transfer irreversible under every possible condition except through direct intervention by the Austrian government.

This was my insurance policy. The government would never intervene unless there was some kind of crime investigation, like one involving fraud, money laundering or identity theft.

Once I got the money transferred I had a plan, a good plan, but one that Karin naturally wouldn't like, because Karin, desperately not wanting to lose her prestigious playground, became increasingly annoyed at me for wanting to change things. The first time I told her about Linkov, she laughed at me and told me no one would pay the kind of cash I was asking for. I started to see that she was no longer the ally and friend I thought I had married. Now that I had sold it, however, she definitively agreed to move to Monaco. For a moment it looked like my stock with her was going up again, until one day while we were visiting Monte Carlo I told her about my idea of going to America, something that wasn't in her vision. But I knew my goal was practical and that, in some manner, I would win out.

Nonetheless, although I was quite sure intellectually that the wire transfer would come, bringing security with it, there was an unfamiliar component in my psychology. Instead of rejoicing every time I thought of the impending move, fear, in fact, very great fear, seemed to mingle with the excitement. Despite the optimism I should by all rights experience in every fiber of my being, my heart and brain were synchronized in a rising tide of psychological terror. Why? I should be resting easy!

Well, there were some reasons to be at least slightly concerned, at least about the move to the U.S. For one thing, my English was not too great—in fact, it was dismal. I could manage with small sentences like "How are you doing?" or "Nice day, isn't it!" and simple stuff like that, but if someone talked to me about a business deal, I would probably go mute. Not a very good platform to make big money, a goal that I generally set for myself—and, until this time, had always attained.

CHAPTER
5

U.S.—The Dream

"Hans, I don't want to leave Monaco."

I was sitting on my little yacht reflecting on these things when I heard a familiar voice shout out, "Hans!" It was Karin. She was dragging Philipp along the pier towards the *Macau*. Philipp had other ideas about his destination and was trying to drag his mother towards the beach. He had a little plastic pail and a tiny shovel, and he wanted to go to work. But Karin was bigger and she wanted to see me—and she, as usual, was winning.

Compared to the general run of couples in Monaco, Karin and I were probably not average, but we were close. When you walked down the streets of Monaco out of season, you would notice a very typical couples' profile. The guys were all in their fifties or sixties, mostly retired, mostly members of the Landed Gentry Club—in other words, very wealthy, successful and secure, part of the Monaco establishment. Their wives were around thirty, usually quite beautiful, and typically carried around a two or three-year-old. I don't think I ever met a couple there with that profile who wasn't on their second or third marriage. Karin and I weren't exactly in that demographic, but this was my second marriage. I was thirteen years older than my wife, and Philipp was two-and-a-half. If you squinted slightly, we were close enough to be members of the Club.

Karin climbed into the yacht, sat down in a semi-comfortable deck chair and sighed with fatigue. My son began to investigate some coils of rope that were trailing around on the deck. Soon she was speaking to me in that strange new tone of hers—one of compassion, even love, but mingled with something bordering on—well, something like contempt.

"I looked all over for you. Do you still have that headache?"

"Yes."

"Well, I don't want to bother you. You probably need to be alone."

"No bother."

"I keep thinking about your plan. I must tell you frankly, Hans, I don't want to leave Monaco. I like it here—finally you've done something good for us, even though you've sold our *Freizeittempel* and you knew I loved that place."

"It needed to be done."

"So you say. As far as the club is concerned, I certainly don't give a damn. It was just a stupid playground for you and your ignorant friend Fritz Titzer. But now you're trying to take away the thing that I love the most, Monaco."

"Three million dollars is not a lot of money here, Karin," I tried to explain. "And I can't do business on an equal footing with most of these people. Not yet. I need a larger playing field—one that actually lets you make money, like the United States."

"Three million dollars, Hans! Come on! It's plenty! And there are plenty of rich people here to do deals with ...."

"I'm sorry, but these people are flipping oil companies, whole islands and multi-million dollar mansions and yachts—they're way out of my league."

"Look, Hans, neither you nor I know English, and Philipp has barely started on his own language."

"That's why I think I should go first, find a place to stay and try to get something started with Manfred."

"That's fine for you to say, but I don't want to leave here."

"I know you like living near rich and famous people, I know you love this high-flying lifestyle, but if you think about it, even with three million dollars, the clock is ticking."

"I know you think what you are doing is best," she said in a conciliatory way. "But you're right; I love it here. I hope you change your mind and find some way to stay."

"Don't hold your breath, darling. We have to leave; Manfred will help."

Karin and I both liked Manfred. He was an interesting guy. He had invented a potentially very valuable air filter that could be used in homes and offices, built from components used in the infrared technology for cleaning the air in a surgical environment. Very valuable.

But it was as if she didn't hear me or didn't want to. "Look, it isn't that I don't like Manfred. I really enjoyed his hospitality when we were on vacation in America and visited him in Houston. His wife was nice too. And it doesn't matter to me that his kids are ignorant little brats."

"But live with him and his family? No way! Not for two weeks and not for two days! There is no way!"

"What do you propose, then?" I said.

"Okay, since you want to go so badly to the U.S. and you believe you can do such great business there, go with my blessings. I won't say another word. When you've made a big success out of yourself and got a lot of cash, then Philipp and I will come and try to live there. But I'll tell you right now, I don't think I can live in America.

"There are no people on the streets in the U.S.—unless maybe you go to a big city. It's weird. I feel totally isolated. And I love Monaco. It's so small—I can walk around with Philipp and it's always safe and beautiful, with lots of interesting people to meet. As far as I'm concerned, for the time being, you can go work over there in the U.S. And when you have time, you can come and visit us here—then go back again."

Just listening to her made me restless and angry. "What kind of bullshit is that?" I said. "We're a family and I want to see my son grow up."

"Look Hans, you already tried to make money with Manfred on the American Cooler. Remember? He stayed with us in our hotel for three whole weeks. You spent a lot of money promoting the Cooler. I remember you renting that yacht on the Blue Danube, inviting the entire Russian delegation, whom you arranged to be officially invited by the Austrian government."

> SOMETIMES YOU HAVE TO SPEND MONEY TO MAKE SOMETHING HAPPEN ...

Yes, I thought, *that was a fabulous time. It was my good friend Peter Razzi, the secretary of the Socialist Party in Austria, who came up with the idea. We had more than 100 people on the yacht.*

"So?" I said aloud.

"So—I remember the live music, fabulous food, the exotic drinks and, of course, the never-ending vodka. And who was paying for it all? You!"

"So? Sometimes you have to spend money to make something happen, Karin. You've seen me do that often enough."

She looked at me skeptically. "Oh, I forgot—there was Mr. Klimascheck and his so-called millions. They never arrived, did they? Even though you had a contract with him for worldwide distribution of the Cooler."

"That's life, Karin," I said, not really wanting to hear anymore.

"Your life, Hans. All we got from that wonderful contract was invaded two years later by the tax revenue service. They put their noses everywhere—in the hotel, in the business, even in the drawers of our bedroom bureaus, looking for anything to link you to your good friend 'Klimascheck.'"

"They didn't find anything."

"Yeah, we were lucky that time. But that wasn't the only million dollar deal of yours that ended up creating nothing but trouble. Not for you, Hans, because you like it. But you see, I don't. I've had enough living like this—under this type of stress." She started to talk louder.

"I've had enough, are you getting this, Hans? Are you registering this?"

I nodded grimly. What was the use of talking?

"I have had enough. Period. Now that you finally accomplished something through this deal with that atrocious little man, you're planning on taking everything I love away from me."

"I am trying to be practical, Karin. For God's sake—"

"For God's sake yourself, Hans! You're making me move to a place where I don't want to be. You're forcing—"

I interrupted her, "You know what your real problem is, Karin? You want to live like a millionaire, but you're not willing to pay the price. The price is higher risk, more work and a little bit of sacrifice. You only want to take, but you don't like to give."

She began to clam up. I was really pissed at her, but on the other hand I knew she was partially right.

The Manfred story started years before I met Karin, when Manfred had an engineering company with his brother in Austria. We met each other during the time when I had a car business with a dealership and body shop, and we became friends. At some point Manfred moved to Houston, and every time he came back to visit his parents he came over and told me how great it was to live in Texas, and all his great ideas for making money. He assured me we could make it really big over there, and I liked that idea just fine.

Once I finally visited him in Houston and he showed me around, I got very excited again. This was around the time I started to date Karin. A couple of months later I sent him $80,000 and he created Liberty, Inc.—our first partnership. He worked industriously to develop the design for the American Cooler and successfully filed for a design patent.

The second time I visited Manfred, with Karin, she did not like America at all. But the reality is, in the end, Manfred and I didn't do so well with the American Cooler, and Karin was there when it fell apart. Six months ago, when Manfred had called again about patenting a new type of air filter, Karin was strictly against my getting involved with another Manfred creation.

Still, I had had enough of Europe; it was time for me to go. Perhaps this would be a way to finally get a fresh start in a new country with a huge market. And I trusted Manfred. If I came to America, he had a nice big home and I could stay there until I was ready to settle in somewhere else. Who knows, maybe we could rev up the air filter project and make big money right away. In that case, I might be able to infuse a little bit of capital to push things forward.

At that moment, though, I still did not have three million dollars, which would have given me time to move and create new resources. What I had was around $50,000: chump change in Monaco—for many, an all-too-short visit to a Casino on a bad night. This was clearly not enough to make any kind of intelligent plans.

Karin sighed with some resolve, as though there was nothing more she could say, which there wasn't. She smiled a little crookedly, gave me a funny look and took Phillip's hand. They were off to the beach. As I watched them go, I thought about Karin's impatience with me.

Marital "Support"

*I liked rubbing my success in their petty
bureaucratic faces.*

Technically Manfred was still my partner. We had a unique
invention, and we could potentially prosper. But whenever I
thought about the guy, I started to feel uneasy. Manfred, not
LINKOV would pop up in my mind. Why? Because starting up
this project, even with a small amount of capital, required something I didn't have yet. No matter what I thought, that $3 million
wire transfer was really rattling my subconscious. The air filter
was the future. This was the present, the uncertain present. My
thoughts turned back to Linkov and the impending deal.

I suppose that now I pay more attention to how I respond to
supposedly great things. Signed contracts, a beautiful woman who
declares her eternal love for you, slaps on the back from important
business people, favorable press—they are like a capricious wind
and can change in a minute. But at that time, more than ten years

ago, I was still hypnotized by it all, and Linkov's clothes, jewelry and cars still blinded me.

Back in Wiener Neustadt, this love and belief in flamboyance was part of my persona. Yes, I was one of the stars of that little town, but not exactly beloved. I drove around in a white Bentley with Monaco plates, which I'm sure seemed very provocative to the municipal government of the town, tiny as it was.

This was my form of rebellion against authority, which I generally hated, and I liked rubbing my success in their petty bureaucratic faces. In the long run that did not really help me at all. And, as I should have known then, when you penetrate the veil, there is often nothing all that real behind fancy cars, expensive real estate and the whole image of affluence. Nothing.

I remember a story that Donald Trump told about coming out of one of his buildings when he was having a bad time in his business. There he saw a man selling pencils. *That man has more money than I do*, he thought. Why? Because Donald Trump owed ten million dollars and probably the man with the pencils had a few coins he could honestly call his own. Still, who would you rather be—the pencil broker or the guy with the real estate?

In truth, even though I seemed to own an expensive bit of paradise, *Freizeittempel* was, in reality, something of a mirage. The Beverly Hills Club was a great idea too, and I was sure that anywhere else in the world it would be a real moneymaker, but the bureaucrats in my home town killed it off. Why the hell did I build everything in Wiener Neustadt, that little home town of mine, and not in Vienna or Salzburg—cities where nobody would give a shit about me? I asked that question of myself many, many times.

Why? Why, why ...!

Nobody would care about it there—but then how could I have shown off in my home town? So I put it there, where I was born and raised, and everyone was jealous and hated my guts. It had been stupid of me, but it was just one of life's lessons.

> THE TROUBLE WITH ME IS THAT I LIKED CREATING SOMETHING, BUT I HATED MAINTAINING IT.

The first time I told Karin that we were losing money and I wanted to sell the *Freizeittempel*, she turned red with anger and tried to slap me in the face. She put her whole self into it, but I was in good shape at the time and caught her hand. "Do that again and you may get a few fingers broken, Dear ..." I warned.

Humiliated, she said, "I trusted you, Hans. We put everything we had into this project and I love it."

"You mean we put everything someone else had into this project and you, baby, you put zero in it. Please be so kind and tell me what you brought to our marriage, your underwear?

"What the hell are you talking about?"

"The bank."

"What's the difference?"

"It's not our money. It's other people's ..."

"Oh, bullshit. What? Are you planning on going bankrupt again?"

"No, I'm not. What the fuck are you complaining about? You've had a great time since you've been with me. In fact, you've gotten everything you wanted from life—haven't you?"

From that point on, Karin never shut up about *Freizeittempel*. She loved that project—and I did, too—but I was never able to make one penny of profit from it. I told her that too, many times, but she didn't like to hear it.

The trouble with me is that I liked creating something, but I hated maintaining it. And although, as I have confessed, I enjoyed promoting myself, I did not really like promoting my business once the initial peak of excitement had passed. As far as business goes, I am probably like an artist who loves to paint, but when he is finished with the painting, no matter how good it is, he wants to get it out of his way, sell it and move on to another painting.

But that was the past. I sat on my yacht and thought carefully about the next steps. To be sure, the transfer should already be done and I should already have the money. Today was Thursday and I would wait the whole of Friday and, if necessary, wait throughout the weekend. It was premature to panic, and any communication, I thought superstitiously, could lengthen the delay. I finally decided that the latest to act would be Monday morning. I would try not to make myself crazy before that.

7

Friday

"But if you come home, you go straight to jail."

It was now Friday morning, which could soon prove to be one of the best days of my life—or maybe one of the trickiest.

I had taken Karin, Philipp and, of course, my little dog to Gerhard's Café. Gerhard's was located in Fontvieille, where I had my apartment. Gerhard, the owner, was from Austria like me. He was a great guy and I really liked him. Like many people who hung out in Monaco, Gerhard, now 38-years-old, had his own unique story.

My friend had been born and raised in Vienna. As a kid he was privileged to be a member in the *Wiener Saengerknaben*, The Vienna Boys' Choir, one of the most famous boys' choirs in the world. Getting into that choir was like getting into Yale or Harvard business school. You had to be very smart and disciplined, and you had to study quite a bit to achieve the level of excellence required by an internationally renowned musical organization like the

Choir. But despite the Choir's prestige, Gerhard was restless and longed for novelty. At seventeen, he escaped from that perfectly organized and disciplined world and attempted to join the French Foreign Legion. If he succeeded, he would trade the comfort and security of a coveted musical career for high adventure, a life of continual, unexpected hardship and possibly the sight of his own blood.

The French Foreign Legion is a unique part of the French Army established in 1831, specifically created for foreign nationals wishing to serve in the French Armed Forces. The Legion recruited pretty nearly every criminal troublemaker in the world. Gerhard soon found himself sequestered with a tough elite unit in the deserts of Algeria—a strange calling for a seventeen-year-old musical prodigy who was rapidly being transformed from a choirboy in Vienna to a killing machine in the African desert. Gerhard's luck did not hold out—the authorities found out he was only seventeen. You had to be at least eighteen-years-old to join the "Fun Club," so they sent him packing.

Once home, he made an immediate decision—to run away again. This time he succeeded in being hired on a cargo ship. When he crossed the equator the first time, he performed the global ritual of seafarers known as the "Equator Christening." In the past, this was often very brutal and degrading for first-time voyagers, but today it is performed mainly for fun and entertainment. In Gerhard's case, he got totally drunk and had a tattoo emblazoned on his stomach. It was a large portrait of the earth, depicted in beautiful but very strong colors, with a big sailing ship in the center. To this day, you will never see him without a shirt.

For the next couple of years, Gerhard continued working on this ship, followed by a long stretch of time when he worked for various wealthy business owners, taking care of their fabulous private yachts. Then one day he was introduced to Adnan Koshoggi, the famous Turkish/Saudi Arabian billionaire, an arms dealer and businessman well-connected to high society and the super wealthy.

Koshoggi had a shrewd eye for talent. He immediately offered Gerhard the position of First Boatman on his huge private yacht, which he customarily moved for a couple of months each year to Monaco. One day, during his annual visit, my lucky friend had the opportunity to partner up with a guy in Monaco, and together they opened up a dealership for yachts, which also did servicing and cleaning.

As far as I am concerned, it was a bright day for me when I first met Gerhard. I was looking for a yacht that day and stumbled into his office. Surprised to discover that we spoke the same German-Viennese dialect, we immediately began to like each other. When we spoke, we were on the same wavelength—it was as if I had already known him for years. By now that feeling and that friendship, which has endured for so many years, has proven my instincts were right. I ultimately bought my yacht from Gerhard, a 47-foot Giorgio, an Italian yacht produced in Pesaro, which is very close to Venice. I christened it the *Macau*.

I was still hanging around Monaco when Gerhard split up with his partner and purchased that little bar and restaurant in Fontvieille that became my second home there. "Gerhard's Café" became a magnet for people to meet people, popular in part because Gerhard could speak fluent English, German, Italian and French, the languages of all our European visitors. His customers loved him creating an improbable mix of people, from call girls to distinguished international businessmen, tennis and

Formula One Racing stars, and everything in between. I even helped him out when he first started. It kept me from getting drunk out of my mind from boredom.

... THERE IS A SEARCH WARRANT OUT WITH YOUR NAME ON IT.

And so, on this very important Friday, I was sitting in my friend's restaurant with my little family and Gerhard when I got a call on my cell phone.

"Hello, Hans speaking."

"Hi, Hans. Helmut Gregor."

Dr. Helmut Gregor was my lawyer in Austria. Why was he calling me?

"Hi, Helmut, what's going on?"

I was about to joke a little with him, make small talk, but there was something in the silence following my question that made it all inappropriate. Something had happened.

"What's wrong, Helmut?" I asked quietly.

He said, "It is almost impossible to believe, but I have a newspaper on my desk and you are on the front page."

"Me?" I said stupidly.

"Yes, you. This article says that there is a search warrant out with your name on it."

"For what, for Christ's sake?"

"For tax fraud!"

"Tax fraud? That's ridiculous. I haven't done anything. You know that!"

"What I know or don't know isn't the point. This is very serious. If you come home, they'll clap you right in jail."

"I get it. You're kidding me. This is your stupid idea of a joke. It's too damn early in the morning for this, Helmut."

"Yah," he said. "I sound very jovial this morning."

"Well ..."

"If you stay in Monaco they can't really touch you. But if you come home, you go straight to jail. You got that, Johann?"

I finally got it. "How is this possible?"

"As far as I can tell, Doctor Lore Hecht, the new IRS Director in your district, went to the prosecutor and convinced him to file a criminal complaint against you. Then they went to a judge and convinced him to write a warrant for your arrest for tax fraud. They want to arrest you because there is a danger you may escape."

"I've already escaped. I'm here, aren't I? I'm living in Monaco with my *Carte de Sejour*."

"I agree. Danger of escape makes no sense."

"This is unbelievable bullshit. Call them and make them back down. Tax fraud? For what? I know Doctor Lore, but I have no idea what I did to her. How could she hate me enough to pull a stunt like this?"

Doctor Lore? Everybody in town knew how she had made her way into power: one affair after the other, bedding down with anyone in the right position to help her in her insatiable lust for advancement. But to choose me as a target? That seemed unbelievable. Why? It couldn't be!

I'm afraid I fell to pieces in front of my friends in the café, screaming and yelling, castigating my enemies, cursing my bad fortune. Eventually, everyone in Gerhard's café was just staring at me. I looked like a madman. To make matters worse, I had forgotten that my lawyer was still on the phone.

I grabbed the cell off the table: "Yeah?"

He was still there. He said quietly, "Hans, please calm down! The whole thing makes no sense. I'll go to the courthouse tomorrow and talk to the judge. Maybe we can fix it; tomorrow is another day."

"Tomorrow?" I said. "Tomorrow is Saturday. You can't do anything on Saturday."

Helmut paused: "Oh yes, you're right. We'll have to wait until Monday. Then we can act. But calm down! Forget about it for a few days. Have a nice weekend, and it'll be okay." He hung up.

I sat down, my shoulders drooping and a look of utter despondence coming over my face. In that moment, I'm sure I looked twenty years older. For a few seconds I prayed that I was dreaming and I would wake up. Three million dollars slipping through my hands and a warrant out for my arrest! What the hell! As if waking from a trance, I slowly began to hear the noises around me and knew it was no dream. The reality I had suddenly encountered was hard-core and refused to go away.

Gerhard and Karin started to ask me what was going on. I told them what my lawyer had told me. Immersed in shock, I still found Karin's reaction rather strange. Instead of seeming anxious, scared or even angry, she was very, very quiet.

Gerhard, on the other hand, tried to comfort me. "Forget Austria," he said. "We both know it's a beautiful country, but it's not friendly to entrepreneurs. That's why I left a long time ago. The same applies to you. So what do you care? You don't have to go back. Nobody can touch you here or anywhere. It's not like you're an international criminal. They aren't hunting for you all over the world. You still have a passport and a *Carte de Sejour*. Forget Austria and be happy. It's sad, but that's the way it is."

Despite Gerhard's well-intentioned reassurances, I still was in a state of blind shock. In any event, I was definitely finished with breakfast. I tried to calm down as I'd been told to do. I turned to Karin and said, "Come on, there's nothing I can do anymore today. Let me take you and Philipp to the beach and, at least, we'll have a nice day."

I tried to pay, but Gerhard refused as usual, like almost every time I tried to pay for myself and my family, saying "Forget it. Save your money. You need it more than I do." We went to our apartment, which was only five minutes away, grabbed all our beach stuff and went downstairs. But I was burned out inside and couldn't believe what Helmut had said.

CHAPTER

8

Reminiscences

My ball of yarn was unraveling a bit more slowly,
but quite steadily ...

W hat had gone wrong in the last couple of years? What the hell was happening? Exhausted and empty, I lay down in a plastic beach chair and quickly began to slip into a trance-like sleep, a sleep that set off a series of journeys into the past. I think it was the trauma that did it—and the incessant questioning about why so much was happening to me at once.

Could it be something like people who face sudden death and tell us that in those few moments they see their whole life spinning before them, like a ball of yarn unraveling at top speed before their astonished eyes? My ball of yarn was unraveling a bit more slowly, but quite steadily—and seemingly without my conscious will. In fact, the process was to go on for days. I seemed compelled to look deeply at my roots, whether I liked it or not.

In my seaside slumber-trance scenes flashed through my mind. I was born in a little town called Wiener Neustadt in Austria on July 14, 1953 into the European Baby Boomer generation, the second child of my parents, Johann and Maria Sitter. My brother, Franz, was two years older than I was. Since my brother was called Franz, we were collectively Franz and Hans. Kind of cute? I think my parents thought so.

This was the time when the Marshall Plan had gone into effect and rebuilding was going on everywhere in Europe, including Austria. The little city of Wiener Neustadt had not escaped the heavy bombing, so reconstruction efforts were intensive.

My grandfather had a decent-sized farm in Oslip, a small village in Austria with a population of maybe 1,200. Oslip was located in Burgenland, one of the nine main provinces of Austria and next to Hungary, so Oslip itself was about three miles away from the border and about 80 miles away from Budapest, Hungary's capital. He also owned the only restaurant in Oslip with a butcher shop. During that time, pretty much everybody in that village owed money to my grandfather. This was a period when people had come back from the War only to find that there were few jobs available. Once activated, the Marshall Plan probably saved a lot of Europeans from starving to death.

My grandfather had a son, Franz, the same name as my brother, as well as a daughter, Maria, my mom. In those days, it was normal that the first-born took over the business and the rest of the property, and any other children would receive his or her inheritance in cash.

In his seventies, grandfather gave everything—the wheat fields, the vineyards, the restaurant, the butcher shop and all the livestock he had—to his son, Franz. Then he bought himself a house across the street from the restaurant, where he lived with my grandmother. The building where the restaurant was also housed a living area and an apartment. My grandfather's gift to his kids was kind of a deal, however. They had to take care of him and his wife as they grew older. As I look at what he did, it was a much better situation than our current assisted living arrangements, where we seem to dump our parents into benign institutions, usually because we can't afford the time or money to take care of them personally. Although it had its challenges for my mom and her brother, it was a sensible, cozy, familial arrangement.

In 1945, the Reichsmark was put out to pasture. The old currency was changed to something called the New Schilling, and everyone received 150 Schillings, while the Reichsmark was devalued to zero. It came all of a sudden—bang! And this devaluation of our currency was a disaster for many, many people. Grandfather lost a ton of money at that time, but for many people it was a lot worse. Quite a few lost everything they had. But during the years prior to the devaluation, he had been shrewd enough to collect an abundance of gold coins. With those, he had enough money to give to my mom so that she could buy a property in Wiener Neustadt, a town in lower Austria about thirty miles away from Oslip. Wiener Neustadt was also around 30 miles south of Vienna, the capital.

My mom's new home had a restaurant, and the second floor had living quarters just like the one of my grandfather's in Oslip. The apartment itself was partially destroyed by the bombing attacks, but it could be rebuilt. Besides, it had a nice garden with huge, beautiful trees and big branches. The whole property was close to an acre in size and located on a corner where the main streets of Wiener Neustadt crossed each other. It was a perfect location for business, since traffic was augmented by the fact that our local high school was located on one of the corners. This then was my mom's share of the inheritance plan. It was the place where I grew up.

Having fallen asleep on the beach, I woke up suddenly, feeling something trickling down on my stomach. I opened my eyes, the memories of that little apartment of my childhood still flashing in my mind. In the blazing light, I saw my son grinning broadly and starting to laugh as I woke up. Then, with a look of intense concentration, he began to draw on the sand he had trickled on my stomach. He gave me a charming little smile and pleaded, "Daddy, please wake up now and play with me in the sand."

I opened my eyes wider and watched him, recognizing how dizzy I felt. I expect I was still recoiling from the shock of the news. *Okay, right now,* I told myself, *you know you can do nothing—so don't destroy everybody's weekend. Be cool and you'll see what's going on Monday.*

Jumping up, I gave Karin a kiss on her cheek and a big hug and said, "You know what, baby—why don't we have a great evening? We can drive to Eze, that little village where the castle is, and have dinner in that great little restaurant."

She looked at me, gave me a real romantic kiss and said, "Great idea. Why not? I think everything will be okay. Up until today you've always fixed everything, every time. Yes, let's go out and have a great evening."

"Okay then," I said, "I'll jump in the sea with Philly and play a little with him. Then we'll go home, take showers and get ready for a wonderful evening. I know Philly will love that castle." I could imagine how much fun it would be for him to explore the narrow little alleys between the ruins, right above the breathtaking panoramic view of our little port below. I knew I would have loved it as a child.

I ran to Philipp, picked him up and threw him in the air, caught him and threw him up again, and then we ran into the sea. The water splashed over us. He reveled there with the pure pleasure only experienced by small children.

Playing in the waves subdued my misery for a few minutes. Philipp was such a cute kid and his happiness was infectious. As I threw him up again, I caught a glimpse of Karin smiling at us from a distance. I think it was the last time I saw her smile so broadly. But at that point, I was still in love with her and hypnotized by our seeming good fortune in the past.

Full of love, I looked at my beautiful wife, my handsome, sweet little son and thought, *Nobody will destroy our weekend. We will have a great Saturday and Sunday and go from there.* In a few minutes, we walked to our apartment, chatting and laughing. Finally, after what seemed like an eternity, I began to relax.

When we got home, Karin took Philipp and put him in the bathtub. While he played with his rubber toys, singing softly to himself, she came up to me, put her hands around my neck and gave me a long, passionate kiss. Then she whispered in my ear, "Tonight, when the little one is sleeping, I will come to you and I will be very nice to you. You'll see, my darling. I love you." Feeling great, I turned on some romantic music and got ready to drive to Eze. Sitting down on the bed I listened to the music, but for some reason I heard strains of an old song in my head, one I barely remembered. Was it *Monday, Monday* by the Mommas and the Poppas?

It was maybe 6:00 p.m. when we took the elevator down to our garage, where my Range Rover and Bentley were parked. "I guess we'll have to take the Range Rover since we're going through the mountains," I said to Karin.

> I THINK IT WAS THE LAST TIME I SAW HER SMILE SO BROADLY.

We jumped in the car and left the garage, taking the Moyenne Corniche, the main street between Nice and Monaco. At this time of year the street was pretty crowded, but we weren't in a hurry. We knew we wanted to get to a certain point in the hills, where we could see the sunset from Eze.

This was a special treat I didn't want Karin or Philipp to miss. We found a parking lot with space for us immediately. It was very unusual to find parking so easily when you first arrive in Eze, but I suppose it was still early and a lot of the tourists had not returned from the beach. We made our way by foot, trudging up the narrow cobblestone streets to the top of the hill.

Eze is a medieval village, perched like an eagle's nest on a rocky summit overlooking the Mediterranean. The ancient fortified village is crowned with the ruins of its twelfth-century castle, which itself sits on a narrow rocky peak. The castle grounds host the well-known Jardin Exotique. The castle is about 2,000 feet up from the sea, so you have a great view of the coast. We drove up towards it, taking the scenic road from Monaco to the village.

The village of Eze forms a circular pattern around the base of the castle. Its old buildings and narrow streets are almost completely restored, with high, red-brick walls and narrow stone roadways. The narrow roads wound upward to a small, man-made waterfall with its large sign proclaiming the Jardin Exotique Panorama. I had brought my family here many times, and it was always beautiful. We were happy to blend in with the tourists and enjoy together the magical, romantic world of Eze.

In the heart of the village there is a two-story clock tower. As you walk up the tower, you peer down over lovely little shaded square parks and can catch a view of the whole valley. The castle was on a short street near one of the main roads of the town. Along the way, we came across rows of stands selling sweet-smelling herbs. This added to the picturesque, rustic feeling of the village.

Finally we reached a restaurant, the Chateau de la Chevre d'or. We got a table outside on the patio where the view was breathtaking. I ordered Karin a glass of champagne, a Cognac for myself and asked the waiter to bring Philly a Sprite. He was excited, his eyes widening as we all took in the superb view of Cap Ferrat, the Cap d'Antibes and the Gulf of Saint Tropez on the restaurant's colorful outdoor terrace. Also, it was comforting that its staff was happy to speak to us in German. When the sunset came, it was beyond words.

Enchanted by our surroundings, we chose a spectacular dinner to complement the magnificent view before us. We began with crab spring rolls in wasabi mayonnaise, followed by duck breast with *fois gras* and truffles. As usual, the food was ample and satisfying but not overflowing, encouraging us to eat slowly, enjoying the subtle flavors and the last, dying rays of the sun.

By early evening, I saw my son's eyes light up as we enjoyed a chocolate mousse with strawberries. Philipp, by now a little gourmet, happily ate alongside us as Karin and I drank wine and toasted our future.

That evening acted as a soporific, dousing my troubles in a blaze of culinary enchantment, splendid wine and the heavenly artistry of the last waves of color dancing on the ocean at night's beginning. Given the challenges of the last few days, and Karin's seeming dedication to me in spite of it all, I felt the apex of my love for her.

Instead of prolonging the inferno of waiting for the intransigent wire transfer, the evening was like a harbinger of the good life to come. Its subtle pleasures burned into my mind like a celestial branding iron imprinting in my soul a sizzling signature of unexpected hope.

When we arrived at home, I carried our sleeping son to the apartment, gave him a goodnight kiss and closed his door. After that final glance at my son, Karin and I disrobed, beginning hours of deep, unyielding passion that would cap the evening with sweet and profound depths of lovemaking that I had rarely experienced in my life. I gave myself to my wife, drowning in her love and beauty and willing surrender, feeling like a king in a coronation of profound sensuality, and she gave me everything she had promised me at the start of the evening. By its end, her profound, undaunted passion had mirrored the glory of the sunset we had savored in the Chateau de la Chevre d'or.

After these last amazing hours we sank into oblivion together—I, lulled by the explosive passion of the night, she, perhaps by some kind of emotional and sensual acrobatic exertion whose intention, after so many years, I still cannot assess or comprehend.

It would be our last peaceful sunrise together.

Weekend in Monaco

"Monaco is a sunny place for shady people."

The next morning was Saturday and all things considered, I was in great spirits. I woke up around 9:00 a.m., went to my balcony and enjoyed my kingly view of Fontvieille. By this time I had buried most of my doubts and was ready to continue making the best of this glorious weekend. As a sequel to that wonderful Saturday evening, I thought it would be great to take my little family to have Sunday brunch in the Café de Paris.

Enveloped in restored hope, I did not think about my shrinking bank account or the warning bells so clearly sounded by the delay on the money transfer. Coming in from the balcony, I gazed admiringly at my beautiful wife sleeping naked, streaked with the sunrays streaming through the rustling translucent silk curtains. I woke her gently with a kiss and whispered, "Are you ready for the Café De Paris?" She yawned and stretched slightly, smiling all the while.

The Café De Paris was one of her favorite places, where she could gape uninhibitedly at the super-rich and, at the same time, could show off herself as well as Philipp, our beautiful kid, and even Umberto. We were well-known to most frequent visitors and residents in Monaco, and Karin, in particular, gave off the sexy ambiance of a classy young mother who warranted the companionship and attention of the rich and famous.

We were part of the scene. Karin, with Philipp, me and the dog, made a nice little Sunday morning attraction for voyeuristic tourists who liked to speculate on the wealth and notoriety of the denizens of this fabulous place.

After waking Karin, I went to Philly's little bedroom, where he was already playing with Umberto in his bed. They were one heart and soul, and it was obvious how much they loved each other. They were a Walt Disney movie all by themselves, that touched everybody's heart.

"Hi, Philly! Are you ready to have brunch in the Café de Paris?" I asked.

"Yes, Daddy," he said, jumping into my arms, his little arms encircling my neck as he kissed me and said, "I love you, Daddy. Can Umberto go with us?"

"Sure. You think I'd leave my bodyguard at home?" I laughed.

So we all got ready. Karin made herself up like a model and dressed Philipp like a kid in a fashion magazine. I was easier on myself, slipping on my Armani jeans and a nice shirt, and was ready in a minute or two. We went down the elevator to our parking lot and climbed in the Bentley. Its prominent Monaco plates would assure us a parking space on the Place du Casino.

We drove to the Café de Paris and stopped in front of the restaurant. In less than ten seconds, a valet was helping Karin and my son out of the Bentley, parking it amongst a sea of Ferraris, Rolls Royces, Bentleys and Lamborghinis. The Place du Casino is noted for its conspicuous displays of expensive and exotic cars. The secret is simple—all the other cars are hidden out of sight in its garage.

The sight of all these cars—their visual boasting of wealth and beauty—adds to the enjoyment of its less affluent visitors, who now enthusiastically mingle with the wealthier guests, their less than perfect transportation safely tucked away from the ogling eyes of the tourists streaming through this vortex of the Monaco experience. Tons of strikingly attired visitors walk through the Place du Casino day and night.

The Café de Paris itself is premium Monaco real estate, located in front of the Casino and the Hotel de Paris. Despite the 24/7 high-fashion parade before you, you can dress as casually as you like and eat in the Café. There are a multitude of families with young kids who had joined us for brunch, and the happy noise of the children gave a nice morning ambiance to our little celebration.

Most of the visiting families there were lucky to have gotten in—because on a weekend you had to have reservations ahead of time. But as someone who had been visiting this place regularly for a year, I was treated differently than a tourist. I had tipped well, particularly in the off-season when the staff was needy, and now everyone who worked there looked on me as a regular and appreciated my business.

To an extent, after so many years, I can say that although I can appreciate this show of wealth and this desire to flaunt oneself before the super-rich world of Monaco, the ostentation of it all has lost a great deal of its charm for me. I covet wealth in and of itself much less these days, and I am seldom impressed by wealthy people per se. Oh, I still appreciate wealth for what it can do, but less for the emblems of status it can buy.

Back then, I thought that wealth and its symbols were meaningful and even important. So when we were greeted warmly by Jeanette, who kissed all of us in the French way, on both cheeks, it was like a public announcement that we were cool people, probably here all the time and undoubtedly rich. This spotlight on us burned even brighter when she seated us in a perfect place in front. Again, I am not so impressed now—but back then, knowing that people always see the table you are placed at as a sign of your status, I was honored by her efforts.

It's not that Jeanette was being insincere, but we all knew that her attention was a form of highly desirable public branding—it just went with the territory. Philipp got the biggest hug and kiss of all. He was pleased as punch about it, without a thought of how the world took it—he was too busy staring at the world around him with those great big eyes and the dog with the floppy ears beside him.

We ordered our usual brunch with double espresso for me and Mimosas for both of us. We had a blast, eating, drinking and watching everyone who walked by, including some tourists gawking at the expensive cars they walked past before they entered the restaurant. Their excitement was as tangible as mine was muted by the trauma of the last few days. I don't remember who created the saying, but it was probably a writer: "Monaco is a sunny place for shady people." In contrast, this area, the hotel and the Café de Paris, is one of those rare places where elegant, sunny people can come and play at the shady life. To some extent I shared the tourists' naïve envy of all this wealth and their desire to emulate it.

As I sat there with Karin and Philipp on that perfect Sunday, gazing at the crowd with a certain amount of sympathy and a strangely mingled element of pity, the strands of that damn song by the Mommas and the Pappas floated through my head again. It was rapidly replaced by the forlorn stone image of Ozymandias, which came flooding involuntarily into my imagination. There is probably no one reading this that was educated in America or Britain who has not read the poem *Ozymandias* by the romantic poet Percy Bysshe Shelley. They most probably forget the poem as soon as they read it, but it was the one English poem I memorized in Austria. Some say it's the best short poem in the English language, and one of the most beautiful sonnets. Yet my thoughts of that image in this happy but deceptive place seemed out of control, a barometer for a peculiar subterranean depression I was beginning to experience. The image of Ozymandias haunted me the first time I encountered it, but why here?

WAS THIS A BAROMETER FOR A PECULIAR SUBTERRANEAN DEPRESSION I WAS BEGINNING TO EXPERIENCE?

Ozymandias is the name of an ancient king, the remnants of whose stone sculpture lie in the desert, consisting of two huge "trunkless" legs and a shattered head. The sonnet ends as an "antique traveler" stares at a pedestal, which says,

'My name is Ozymandias, King of Kings:
Look on my works, ye Mighty, and despair!'
Nothing beside remains. Round the decay
Of that colossal wreck, boundless and bare,
The lone and level sands stretch far away.

As I sat there eating, the light around me seemed to flicker strangely. The bubbly tourists and parading celebrities for a few seconds seemed to fade. The whole scene seemed to be penetrated by a subdued x-ray light, and I saw skeletons, as in some old Mexican etching celebrating the *Dia del Muerte*, chewing on delicate pastries and sipping their perfect shots of espresso just like we were. Delicate skeletons, penetrated by the soft light of a Monte Carlo morning, flaunting their indelicate toothy grins as they showed off their jewels and designer fabrics, their bones glowing slightly in the all-seeing rays of that strange light.

This was a brief, terrifying vision. I believed in nothing really then, but I had heard of Tibetan Buddhist exercises where the practitioner drinks from skulls and sleeps in graveyards to prepare him for his inevitable death.

Calm and Love Before the Storm

As I lay there Sunday night, my eyes barely opened,
I dared to speculate that a new life, full of promise,
was ahead for me and my happy little family.

Had my imagination become a graveyard for these strange images? But just then, as I pondered my impending descent into psychosis, the touch of my boy's little hand on my wrist quickly pushed me into the softer daylight of the real world.

"Daddy, can we go to the zoo? Can we, Daddy?"

"Maybe tomorrow, my dear."

Karin looked at me with eyes that longed to please our son, and I knew then for sure that we would be off in that direction that very day. We spent the rest of the day on the yacht with a brief visit to the beach, relaxing together and playing with Philipp.

Around two in the afternoon on Sunday, we were off again along the coast, taking the route down the Moyenne Corniche to St. Jean Cap-Ferrat, a seaside village between Monaco and

Nice. There you can find the real beauty of the peninsula and the lovely sheltered bay, even though it is heavily residential, with very expensive homes mostly hidden behind high fences and ubiquitous signs announcing the invisible presence of local security.

The village itself is rather small, but there are a lot of nice terrace cafés—restaurants, most of them along the port—like many along this part of the coast, a small fishing port that evolved into larger yacht harbors.

> MY GOAL FOR THIS SUNDAY WAS TO GIVE PHILIPP THE TIME OF HIS LIFE.

Cap-Ferrat has three different beautiful beaches, but also a big zoo with more than 300 animals, including mountain bears, tigers, rhinos, giraffes and much, much more. My goal for this Sunday was to give Philipp the time of his life. I tried to mentally photograph everything—the slightest vista, the most remote promontory, the slenderest thread of white sand—thinking that my future soon might not give me access to this paradise.

We wound around fifteen miles of that beautiful scenic road until we were far up in the hills. When we arrived, we parked right next to the zoo and bought tickets, staying there the whole day until it closed at 6:00 p.m. I think Philipp enjoyed the mountain bears the most, watching them clap their hands to induce the tourists to throw them food. It was lovely to walk around, holding Karin's hand with our little son tagging along. It was as though we had fallen in love all over again. Or so I thought.

After the zoo, there was a little carnival. Philipp found a go-cart to ride in, and the only unpleasantness I felt that day was when I had to separate him from the little car and the circle of friends he had found. He was very tired and fell asleep on the way home. After putting him to bed, we looked at each other ravenously and passed the remainder of the evening—as before—satisfying our hunger for each other. Our gentle moans echoed throughout the tiny bedroom until our passion was resolved in the wee hours of the evening.

It was a kinder, perhaps friendlier repetition of the night before. Quietly passionate, but just as urgent. If Friday evening was a climax of love and commitment, Sunday evening was the dénouement, a relaxation of raw passion into the tender mercies of what seemed to me as pure a love as I had ever experienced.

As the evening drew to a close, I promised myself that the next day I would call the bank and pressure them to finalize the transfer of my money. I was now relaxed, supercharged by Karin's attentions and the conspicuous happiness of my son that day. As I lay there Sunday night, my eyes barely opened, I dared to speculate that a new life, full of promise, was ahead for me and my happy little family.

After a while, I noticed that I wasn't sleeping. Still happy and confident, I poured myself a shot of brandy. Well, I thought, I'm still not sleepy, but I feel confident and good about Monday. So I took another shot, and another and another. Sometime later I passed out, I don't remember exactly when, but I wasn't surprised at my hangover the next day.

11

Monday, Monday

"I'm sorry, Hans, but I don't have great news for you."

I woke up and looked at my watch. It was still the 18K gold Rolex Day Date with a Presidential band that I bought from Ference Barat, a good friend of mine who dealt a lot in diamonds, expensive watches and jewelry. I bought it for six grand 20 years earlier. I loved this watch—although I had to put it in a pawnshop several times on my road to success—but I bought it back every time. Ever since, more than any person I knew, I trusted my watch and was certain that it was, indeed, exactly 7:15 a.m. Monday morning. It was the day I had waited for impatiently, then drunkenly, throughout the entire weekend.

And that whole weekend, I had been haunted by the American song *Monday, Monday* by The Mamas and the Papas. I really could only remember the first verse:

Monday Monday, so good to me,
Monday Monday, it was all I hoped it would be ...

The first two lines were fine, but why did I have to think about the second two lines that went:

Oh, Monday morning, Monday morning couldn't guarantee ...
That Monday evening you would still be here with me.

Ridiculous. One glance told me that Karin and Philipp were still sleeping. Maybe my wife was a bit "complex," but she still loved me. I was about to collect three million dollars and all was well with the world. So in high spirits for the moment, I slipped out of bed and tried not to make any loud noise that would wake them.

Umberto, on the other hand, was already up. Like me, he respected the state of his other sleeping masters, looked at me with his big doggy eyes and wagged his tail silently. As I nabbed a can of dog food from the cupboard and hunted down a can opener, I started to organize my priorities for the day.

One of the nice things about Monaco was that it inhabited the same time zone as Austria, so it took very little to coordinate schedules with my associates at home. I knew the Court would open in a few minutes, at 8:00 a.m., and that would be about the time that my lawyer had the first crack at the judge. It could take him an hour or more before he finished. I had time to tramp down to Gerhard's Café and have a croissant and espresso. Thank God! I left the apartment with Umberto and walked over there, relatively optimistic, despite all the drama of the previous week.

Angelique had the morning shift at Gerhard's. She was a sexy little thing, with dark hair, soft brown eyes and an inviting figure. Did she have a crush on me? I didn't think so, but I paid too much attention to her morning kiss, realizing suddenly that I was compounding the morning's complexity by bothering about such a thing. I decided that her pleasant "Bon Giorno, Hansi!" as she stooped down to pet Umberto was just a splendid little act of friendship, and that was enough. I sat down at an elegant white wrought-iron table on the corner of the terrace.

"Bon Giorno, Bella," I said. "What are you up to today?"

"Nothing, Hans. You look a little sad. Are you not well?"

"I had a horrible headache last night, but I finally got some sleep. I think I'm all right."

"Good. Your usual, then?" She looked at me. "And, ... no ... Gerhard's not here on Monday mornings, of course. He was up late as usual last night."

I owed a lot to Gerhard. For one thing, many of those yacht owners on the pier at Fontvieille had to wait for years to get a yacht slip, but not me. Why? Because my good friend Gerhard, a renowned local bon vivant, was also a good pal of the Harbor Master, a key dignitary here. This particular Harbor Master could not be bribed or impressed with a stack of money. In fact, certain wealthy people had gone that route and had wound up living out their lives without a yacht slip. You need friends like Gerhard to survive in this world.

Angelique came up to me, handed me a German newspaper and tried to chit-chat with me, but I wasn't able to make much small talk, and eventually she left. Now I was alone, waiting for three million dollars that was three days late. The day of the transfer had fallen on a Friday. Maybe it was just a bad timing problem. Ever wonder why when money is transferred to your account—or when money is transferred from one of your accounts to another—it often takes a few days? Or why they might charge you ten bucks or more to make a transfer? Why are there always these little delays? *Interest*, my friend. The power of *interest*—to hold money as long as possible. All those little bits of money add up to a bonanza of *interest* for the banks.

And if they can find a way, banks use penalties to make us pay for the interest by our little indiscretions. If the money is not paid on time, if it is transferred too quickly out of their hands, if someone in the bank has to hit an extra button—or, God forbid, they have to reach into their computerized archives to find a lost check—they are going to charge you. Maybe the hold-up was just one of those mechanical glitches. Even a one-day bit of three million dollars would be nice for a bank, a serendipitous commercial delay. And so I tried to rationalize the delay.

I loved it here in Monaco, and whatever my plans, I certainly didn't want to leave. Right now, all we had was a little bedroom apartment with maybe about 400 square feet of space. But from its small balcony I had a perfect view of the port in Fontvieille, where my yacht was parked. The port itself was surrounded by a high, steep rock wall. On the top was the famous castle where the Grimaldi Family lived, from which Prince Rainier ruled Monaco.

Fontvieille was the newest of the four traditional districts in the principality of Monaco. It is located in the western part of a newly constructed area reclaimed from the Mediterranean during the 1970s. The district has a population of something like 3,000 in an area of 0.2 square miles.

From my balcony, I could see my yacht and all the other huge yachts in the port. I could also see the school where Philipp went every week. It was the same school where Princess Stephanie sent her children. Every time, when I looked from my fourth floor balcony, I was excited and happy.

Yes, Monaco is a fabulous country. Still, it is the second smallest country in the world. Only the Vatican is smaller. And while the view from my little apartment was breathtaking, so also was the rent and what we had to pay for day-to-day, ordinary living expenses. My rent back then was $3,000 a month, the slip for my yacht was $2,000, and believe it or not, to eat

... FOR THE ORDINARY PERSON WITH AN ORDINARY LIFESTYLE, LIVING IN MONACO WOULD SEEM ALMOST INSANE.

and have a little bit of fun you could easily ring up another $15,000 a month. A little math would show that with a piddling $50,000, I had less than three months of survival time in Monaco. This is what happens when you belong to a club that you flat out can't afford to live in with chump change.

But there was still a bright side. When I received my $3 million in Monaco, I would not have to pay one penny of tax, whereas if I had received this money in Austria, I could have only retained 20 to 40 percent of it. That would have put a positive damper on any plans to move and capitalize a business. Back in 1992, I had already filed for a *Carte de Sejour* so that I could receive money from real estate commissions transacted outside of Austria without them having any legal right to tax my income at those astronomical rates. As you can imagine, this form of tax relief was not at all appreciated by the Austrian government, but it was legal and they really could do nothing about it.

The City Fathers naturally didn't want Monaco to become a ghost town where people signed up for a mailbox with a fake residential address and then split. That's why in order to get the *Carte de Sejour*, you had to have an apartment there and be living there more than six months a year. In a way, for the ordinary person with an ordinary lifestyle, living in Monaco would seem almost insane.

There are parts of Monaco, for instance, where you can cross the street from your own apartment and be in France, where the same apartment that you are paying $3,000 for in Monaco now costs you only $400 per month. In other words, you are paying a high price for the freedom from income tax. But to the super-rich, it is more than worth it. Believe me. And someone like me—a straggler between ordinary and celestial financial realities—could slip in for a while.

Now if I were aspiring to purchase a home or a house, it would be a completely different story. To own a real house in Monaco is reserved only for the richest people on Earth. For instance, scaling down that concept for a moment, a humble little 400-square-foot apartment like mine would cost about $600,000 in Monaco, but only about $80,000 in France. It was clear to me that—three million or not—we had to leave. Besides my work with Manfred, I had another idea.

In 1987, Dietrich Mateschitz started his energy drink, Red Bull. But back in the nineties, when he had just started, he found himself on the brink of bankruptcy. Perhaps because he was lucky and had a strong family, he was able to go to his grandmother and borrow something like $200,000. The rest of his family stuck with him and he survived. It took five years, but his energy drink eventually took off and Red Bull spread to Hungary, Germany and Switzerland. I had met Dietrich two times in my life. He was amazing and very tough, but at the same time, smart and charming.

I already had a formula for a new energy drink and had found a company that would produce it for me. All I needed was capital and a perfect name. Of all the many names I thought of, I preferred "Sitter's Liberty—the energy drink that sets you free." I envisioned a blazing white can with the Statue of Liberty standing tall in the background.

This was my first choice, but I didn't stop there. I kept thinking and thinking because the name had to be perfect. I played around with hundreds of names and marketing ideas. I was enthralled with capturing the American market. Mateschitz had already made millions with his drink, but in the U.S., nobody till now had a clue about energy drinks. Imagine, nobody in Coca Cola country seemed to know how big a fire Red Bull was lighting in Europe, and it didn't take a seer to predict that one day soon it would charge into America. I wanted to be the matador that slowed that Bull down. I wanted to be first in America with an energy drink.

So I sat there for several hours wondering about the damned money, pretending to read the newspaper while I tried to shore up my nerve. After a while, right there in Gerhard's, I started to pray. And do you know what? As I prayed, I became even more nervous and my headache began to return. What was up with that?

After I had glanced at the paper maybe fifty times, I decided to return to my yacht. Maybe I could think more clearly there. Taking some water out of its refrigerator, I felt dehydrated and sad. As soon as I sat down on the aft deck, my cell phone began to ring. Damn, it was Helmut! My heart started to pound. "Well?" was all I could muster.

"I'm sorry, Hans, but I don't have great news for you. The prosecutors have refused to cancel the warrant. If you come home, they will arrest you—for sure."

The Warrant Remains—No Escape

I felt rudderless and without any clear direction.

I was quiet for a time, trying to assimilate everything. Nothing added up.

"Hello, Hans, are you still there?" Helmut said, after a while.

"Sure, but I don't know what to say. I really don't know."

Helmut said, "Listen, I talked to a reporter from the local newspaper who'd like to write a story about you. They'll send him to Monaco and pay for my ticket too. Believe it or not, I got them to promise that we could read it first and approve its contents. That's very unusual, but given your fragile situation, I had to insist on it. What do you think?"

"I don't know," I said. "What's your advice? You're my lawyer."

"I don't think it can hurt you, and maybe we get some attention and the prosecutors will rethink what they're doing."

I said, "Okay, but do me a favor. Go to the bank and talk to Mrs. Hoffer. Tell her I'm waiting for the money transfer at my hotel."

He said, "Okay, I will, but you need to call her first. And if you agree, I'll call the reporter right now and we'll book a flight." I agreed and hung up.

First of all, I took a deep breath and looked around me. Was I still on planet Earth or had I been magically transported to La-La Land, where nothing whatsoever makes sense? An arrest warrant for nothing! Ridiculous. I decided I should count my blessings. Still, I was amazed at the absurdity of my loss, the injustice and the potential assault on the integrity of my family. And I still didn't know how much was really at stake.

At this point, I was confused as to what I should tell Karin, Philipp or my poor parents, who had enough troubles of their own. How would people who knew me, particularly my parents, react to what would be in the newspaper? If only for them, how could I miss the opportunity to tell my story publicly, in my own hometown paper, in my own words? Probably the only weapons I had were a decent lawyer and some publicity that might be potentially embarrassing for my assailants.

My mom was 76 and my dad was 72. At the time, Dad was paralyzed on one side of his body and couldn't walk following a stroke. He now had to wear Pampers because of incontinence and needed constant care from my mother and various assistants, who ranged from a professional nurse to some friends and an aunt who pitched in a few hours a week. With all that burdensome illness on my mother's hands, how could I explain to her what was happening to her "Hansi"?

Like many older people, she had worked her butt off her entire life in our family restaurant and now deserved to rest and enjoy her life—instead she had to take care of a sick husband. I had always planned on doing more for them, but now I was helpless. I couldn't even see them without being arrested.

Another concern was my brother, Franz. We never had a really great relationship, and I wondered what Franz, as I was already the black sheep of the family, would think and say about me now. Thousands of depressing thoughts raced through my head. I felt rudderless and without any clear direction.

Hell, I thought, I should probably call Mrs. Hoffer, the lady who had handled my transaction with Herr Linkov. Maybe I could pressure her to send the money despite what had happened. As I began to feel my old self come to the fore, I weighed the consequences of calling her ... what could really happen, after all, except that I would have a better picture of where I stood? If I were in trouble, it was only in Austria—not anywhere else in the world. I still had my wits. I was free and capable. I began to feel a sense of peace, at least temporarily. Anyway, the thought was kind of soothing. Then, rightly or wrongly, thoughts of revenge occurred to me—if, indeed, I actually received the money.

I guess it is difficult for me, even now, to tell the difference between out-of-control feelings of revenge and a clear sense of justice, but I know in my heart that the former is somehow wrong and dangerous to one's peace of mind—just because one has been wronged, one gives free rein to one's animal nature. At the time I barely recognized the dangers involved in dwelling on those feelings, and I don't know what would have happened if Gerhard had not acted as my provisional conscience.

I envisioned using my money to get the best lawyers and having them tear Doctor Lore to pieces, disgrace her in public and charge her with criminal fraud. I dwelt, in exquisite detail, on the depths of her lying and envisioned her weeping in jail, contemplating the loss of her reputation and career.

In theory, at least in a theory of retaliatory justice, there is nothing wrong with these kinds of thoughts. But as I have grown as a person, I now see these types of unchecked thoughts of vengeance as a form of high-powered self-destruction. There are better ways to handle situations, ones based on a better, deeper grasp of the human condition and its connection to some kind of intangible, but real, divinity within.

That day, however, I was lost, and without someone to shake me out of it, I easily fell back on my animal nature. Energized by these thoughts of revenge, I saw myself retrieving Mrs. Hoffer's number from the cell and dialing in an enraged trance. A moment later I was on the phone with the lady. This was the real key to my financial salvation. I introduced myself to her, reminding her that "I was with Herr Linkov in your Bank and you were so kind to show me the sufficiency of the account to buy my hotel for three million dollars. Following that discussion, he signed the wire transfer agreement that you gave me and you told me not to worry, that no one could cancel that wire transfer. Is that correct?"

Yes," she sighed, "but I did not, in any way, expect Federal Investigators to come into the bank and freeze all of Herr Linkov's accounts."

I said nothing. I just couldn't speak.

"You have to understand that on Thursday Herr Linkov was arrested, and the next day all his accounts were

OH, MY GOD, I THOUGHT—IS THE WHOLE UNIVERSE AGAINST ME? WHAT COULD POSSIBLY BE NEXT?

frozen and his transfers were cancelled. Another account of his, with five million dollars, is also frozen."

Far from revenge, I now thought—even prayed—that I would have a stroke myself and just fall dead on the ground. My mouth was open, but I didn't know what to say. "I've done nothing wrong. I simply want my money. We are talking about three million dollars, all that I have been working for four years. You can't be serious. Please tell me what I can do!"

She said, "I understand your frustration, but you've had really bad luck. It's out of my hands. I suggest you consult a lawyer."

I said, "You're telling me that if they would have come a couple of hours later, I'd have had my money and they could do nothing about it?"

She said, "That's right, Mr. Sitter."

I didn't know what to say anymore and hung up.

Oh, my God, I thought—is the whole universe against me? What could possibly be next? I'd be flat broke in a few days, unable to go home to see my parents, and humiliated in front of my family and friends.

I sat there in my yacht, my mind going nowhere. I was totally helpless—like a baby without a mother, stranded in a mega-billion-dollar paradise without a nickel to my name ... at least in a matter of a few weeks. I had hundreds of questions, mostly for God, but no one was speaking to me out of the clouds. Wherever I thought God might be, he was not in Monaco that day—or, as I look back, if he was, I certainly wasn't able to see him.

It's hard to describe what was going on in my head when the phone rang again. My hand shaking slightly, I picked up the phone. It was Karin. "Hi, baby, where are you? I miss you already. I brought Philly to class already and I could be ready for you, very ready. Would you like to come up and relax for an hour? You won't regret it, I promise you."

Knowing what had just happened with Mrs. Hoffer, I wasn't sure what to say to her. I just knew I had to buy some time, so I swallowed hard and said, "Baby, I'm really sorry, but as you know I'm working on all that shit that's happened and I need a couple of hours to straighten everything out."

She said, "You sure you're okay? You don't sound too good."

At that moment, I had to use to all my willpower to restrain myself. There was a torrent of pain winding through every pore in my body. If I let myself go, I would pour all that rage and pain into her, further undermining her security and the sense she had that, despite everything, I could handle what was happening. I held back the wild, enraged beast inside me and said quietly, "Everything is fine, baby—I'll call you a little bit later."

After I hung up the phone, everything I held back spilled out onto my yacht and the sea around me. I stood up, began to pace around the deck. Suddenly and uncontrollably, I fell on my knees, screaming and sobbing and yelling at my forgotten God, *"Why? Why is this happening to me? What did I do to deserve all this shit?"*

I started to weep like a little child. I thought I heard some people far off, probably heading to their yacht on the pier, so I headed downstairs. I had a nice little cozy saloon down below, but I was in no mood to mix drinks, so I grabbed a bottle of Jack Daniels from the refrigerator and filled a glass half full of whisky and poured it down my throat. As soon as I felt the soothing warm feeling in my stomach, I poured and gulped down another half-glass with one swallow.

As tears ran down my cheeks, a feeling of complete helplessness came over me. All my life I had thought I was a tough guy, but this was too much for me to handle in one fucking day. I was close to a nervous breakdown and a complete freak-out—which was now rapidly becoming a drunken freak-out. I looked up towards the Grimaldi castle perched on that sleek, 300-foot-high rock wall and watched birds slowly circling in the sky nearby. Why couldn't I jump up and streak up into the sky to join them and leave all my earthly troubles behind?

I was sure that the First Family had its troubles. Grace Kelly had died in a car accident. Princess Caroline's husband had died in a racing boat disaster. Princess Stephanie was consistently in trouble, dominating the front pages with the latest royal scandal— and here I was in the midst of my own pure drama, the only difference between me and them being one of social and economic scale. At least until now, there weren't any Paparazzi huddling in the bushes, but then again, wasn't a reporter on his way?

Although tipsy, I did everything I could to return to a normal state of mind. I started to think. What should I do next, and above all, what should I tell Karin?

13

Gerhard

*"Tomorrow" was submerged in the last real fun I would
have for quite a few months.*

Given my tempestuous state of mind, I decided on a strategy
of temporary isolation so I could rest and regroup before assaulting
the fortress of my dilemmas again. I knew that in this state, I could
easily lose myself in my misery, and I wanted to avoid a violent
argument with anyone whatsoever at this point. Well, perhaps
not total isolation. Gerhard might be in the café by now, so I
decided to head over there. I looked at my watch—it was already
a little past noon. Where had the time flown?

I headed out to the café, my little friend Umberto shadowing
me about fifty paces behind. We arrived soon enough and I
lucked out. Gerhard was there. Angelique was still working, but
they weren't really busy at all. Gerhard saw me and said, 'Hi,
Hansi, what's going on?" He squinted at me. I am sure I was red
as a beet and my hands were shaking, "Are you okay?"

"Hell no! Nothing is okay!" I said.

I think he recognized from the look on my face that I was in the midst of some big drama. "You know, I'm not so busy right now. Let's sit down here and drink a glass of wine together, and you can tell me what's going on."

We did just that. After I finished telling him the whole story, he put on a really serious face and said, "You know, the best thing we can do is take your yacht through La Mala and anchor in the bay. The Café Begin can send out a dinghy to pick us up, and I can take you to lunch. After that we can take a nap, drink some cocktails on the beach, go swimming and come back late in the afternoon. That way you can have a couple of hours rest, forget everything for a while and clear your head." He got up and said, "Come on, let's go."

Not wanting to be rushed, I didn't get up but just sat there thinking about Gerhard's proposal. Then I began to think about an afternoon at La Mala. This was the most secluded, magical, gorgeous beach on the whole Cote d'Azur, and that's saying a lot. I said, "Wait a little bit. I have to tell Karin."

Gerhard said, "Okay. But tell her you're helping me go shopping for the restaurant. And don't ask her to come with us. You need a break, believe me. So make your call and hurry up."

I followed Gerhard's instructions and called Karin, telling her that I was going to help Gerhard with his shopping for the restaurant. She said that in that case she would go fix her nails and hair and pick up Philipp at 6:00 p.m. from kindergarten. We'd meet each other later at the apartment and cook dinner for everyone. She seemed to be happy with the plan. That was all that I wanted— because I had to buy some time. I said, "Great, baby—I'll see you later." Gerhard and I finished our wine and both gave Angelique a kiss goodbye. Angelique was sexy and cute, I was sure of that. Given my state of mind, I was grateful that I could still recognize a beautiful woman. Then we left, walking in the direction of the yacht with Umberto trailing behind us. Once on the yacht, we revved up the two Caterpillar Diesel engines, cast off and left the port at Fontvieille.

Mala Beach was literally around the corner from the port. Five minutes later, we took a turn into the turquoise water that graced the small beach and colorful view of Cap d'Ail, the little village behind it. In the distance we could see the eastern coast of the Cap Ferrat peninsula, which always looks to me a bit like Thailand.

The water was dotted with yachts, and the exclusive beach bar was packed with celebrity visitors, as well as the super wealthy. We dropped the anchor and waited. Within minutes, a rubber boat from the beach bar came and picked us up and brought us to the beach bar. I left Umberto behind in the yacht.

I had gone here many times with Gerhard. Each time we had a blast and got drunk. Gerhard ordered different appetizers like carpazzio, gambas fricassee, and as an entrée, grilled lamb cutlets with vegetables, with a couple of Manhattans as aperitifs and a bottle of Chateau Batailley-Pauillac, which was going at $125 a bottle. It wasn't long before we ordered the second bottle, and soon we were pretty toasted.

We had a great time. For a couple of hours I forgot my misery, and we talked about the good old times and tried to have a bit of fun. He recognized the effort I was making. He saw how I was forcing myself to be gregarious and funny. We even flirted with a couple of girls on vacation from Germany. The girls, as tourists, were totally blown away by the beautiful view. It would have been easy for us to invite them to my yacht—and then we would, for sure, have had a good time. But that type of adventure was the last thing on my mind. All I wanted was to eat and drink like there was no tomorrow—which, in a sense, was beginning to look highly likely. "Tomorrow" was submerged in the last real fun I would have for quite a few months.

It got to be later than expected. When the dinghy brought us back to our yacht, the sun had already begun its slow descent and it was close to 8:00 p.m. We were drunk, but that didn't stop us from dropping our swimsuits as soon as we arrived at the yacht. Alone in this amazing turquoise sea with the sun just a red line on the horizon, we swam happily and vigorously, gazing occasionally at the beautiful limestone cliffs rapidly becoming silhouettes in the fading sun. Knowing that this might be the end of my stay in Monaco, I tried to photograph the scene in my mind, hoping against hope I would not lose my ticket to this paradise.

On the way home with my yacht, Gerhard took over as captain. Despite the swim I was still heavily toasted, but I had to call Karin. I didn't have a lot to say. She recognized immediately how drunk I was and I told her it would be better, considering my situation, that I sleep on my yacht. Gerhard also called his girlfriend, Mireille.

Pretty soon we were back in the port at Fontvieille, tied up to my slip. Considering our level of inebriation, I didn't see how Gerhard could handle the yacht so perfectly, but having been with him over the years in many different boats, I can safely say he was the best captain and helmsman I ever met in my life. Then we walked back to his café to make sure everything was okay. Upon arriving we found that Angelique had left already. Roberto, a charming and reliable server, was working that evening. In his off hours, Roberto played the role of a handsome Italian gigolo, a womanizer and playboy.

In the moonlight filtering into the Café, were my eyes deceiving me as I saw a skeletal hand refilling my mug of Gerhard's best coffee of the day? I looked up—but no skull leered at me, just Roberto's welcoming smile for both of us. "What's up, Hansi?" he laughed. "Are you all right? And what did you do to my boss?"

"Are you kidding? The real question is—what did he do to me?" I asked smugly. It was obvious from our tousled hair, loose laughter and baggy clothes that regardless of our present lucidity, we had recently been drunk as two skunks, dedicated to escaping the confines of ordinary reality. Since the café was not really busy, we invited Roberto to sit with us. In moments, now, all three of us were inebriated in the empty café, filling the room with jokes, laughter and small talk until sleep began to overcome us.

Gerhard walked with me back to the yacht with a brave new bottle of wine from his restaurant under his arm. Though exhausted out of our minds, we lay down on deck chairs and talked until 3 o'clock n the morning. By then the bottle of wine was empty and we raided the downstairs bar for a couple of swallows of whiskey. Before my head hit the pillow, I was in a deep sleep.

Meet the Press

"So what's happened with the money?
Shouldn't that be here already?"

I woke up on the yacht. The first thing I noticed was my headache. It was as if my head were being attacked by shards of angry glass. I looked around the yacht's master bedroom and saw Umberto respectfully sitting in front of my bed. He was waiting until I would finally stand up and feed him. Despite my terrible hangover, I managed to do just that. As Umberto wolfed down his breakfast, I stumbled over to the guest bedroom, only to find that Gerhard had left already. I took a peek at my Rolex and was shocked. It was already 11:00 a.m.

I checked my cell and saw I had missed a couple of calls. First I accessed the message from my lawyer and listened to it. It said, "Hi, Hans, I'm coming tomorrow with the reporter from the newspaper. We're catching a flight on Air France from Vienna to Nice and should make it into Nice at 2:00 p.m. Could you be so kind as to pick us up?" I called him back and confirmed that I would pick him up in Nice.

Then I tried to find my headache pills. My hand was shaking when I finally found them. I took two, wishing that someone would pull out the needles of searing pain rolling around in my head. I lay down a little bit and waited until the pills began to work in my system, softening my discomfort. In ten minutes, I began to feel the pain recede and some life flow into me again. I had to eat something, so I took a fast shower, put on a fresh shirt and pants and headed over to Gerhard's.

When I arrived at the café, Angelique greeted me with "Bon Giorno, Hansi. You're not looking so good this afternoon" and gave me my daily kiss. She didn't have to tell me that I was looking like shit. I knew it already.

I smiled slightly and said, "I had a long, tough night with Gerhard. Where is he anyway?"

She said, "He also isn't feeling so good and went home to lie down. He'll be back this afternoon." I ordered my breakfast after begging her for two more headache pills and sent her a flying kiss with my hands as she laughed and rushed to the kitchen with my order.

A few minutes later I steeled my nerves and called Karin. "How are you? Are you are okay? Philly was asking for you," she said.

"I'm sorry, baby, but all this pressure is driving me nuts. I took a break yesterday with Gerhard. I just needed to get away for one day and have a little bit of fun."

"So what's happened with the money? Shouldn't that be here already?"

I told her that my lawyer was coming with a reporter the very next day, but I was afraid to talk to her about the money transfer and the possibility that we would never receive it.

Towards the end of a very slow, trying day, I picked up Philly at his school and took him back to the apartment for a home-cooked spaghetti dinner. After we had dinner, it was bed time for Philly. I soon followed, making lame excuses about not feeling too well and went to bed. I tried to get my mind straightened out for the next day when I would pick up my lawyer and the reporter. It was the only thing I could think about.

In the morning I got out the Bentley and drove towards the airport in Nice. It was a tedious drive during the summer when tourists flooded every main artery in Monaco. Monaco is easily accessed across its borders with France or Italy by a network of highways. Between Nice and Monaco, there are three main scenic roads: the Basse Corniche (Low Coast Road—Highway 98) along the sea, the Moyenne Corniche (Middle Coast Road—Highway 7) going through Eze, and the Grande Corniche (Great Coast Road) going through La Turbie and Col d'Eze (Eze Pass). All three are pretty drives offering spectacular views over the coastline, but my favorite route was, by far, the Basse Corniche along the sea. It was the longest of the three, but I always loved it. Every time I drove along it I asked myself—how did even God create such a beautiful view?

So I took my time, stopping along the way at a little café with a generous view of the sea. Still nervous from my ongoing ordeal, I was glad to enjoy a leisurely espresso and a Perrier.

After 20 minutes, I climbed back into the Bentley, and by the time I got to the airport, it had taken one hour of driving to travel nine miles. I still arrived at exactly 2:00 p.m.

Helmut called me as I was driving up to the arrival area. He and the reporter were already at customs, and in a few minutes they had exited the terminal and were walking towards my car. Getting out, I shook hands after greeting them.

"Hans, can I introduce you to Martin Repp?" Helmut said. "You'll recall he's a reporter from *Noen*, a newspaper circulating in lower Austria but published in Wiener Neustadt. The newspaper will allow us to approve the text of the article in exchange for exclusivity for the whole story. That's the deal."

I said, "That's fine with me, and thanks for coming anyway. Are you guys hungry?" Helmut and Martin nodded, indicating they were ravenous. Since neither of them had ever visited Monaco, I decided to give them a little sightseeing tour en route to lunch. "What's your schedule?"

"We leave tomorrow at 4:00 p.m.," Martin said. "I need to put this article to bed by Friday so it can go out Monday."

Here we go again, I thought. *"Monday, Monday."*

"We'll have a late lunch in the Café de Paris. We can start work then. But I still want you guys to see as much as you can of this place. I've traveled all over the world, but nothing touches Monaco."

I took the same route back as before. We passed the Hotel Negresco on the promenade des Anglais on the Baie des Anges in Nice. The Hotel is striking. Martin gasped, "Oh, my God, what's that?"

I smiled. "This is the famous Hotel Negresco. If I remember correctly, it was built around 1900 by Henry Negresco, who came from Romania. The Hotel has a complex history. Its ups and downs remind me of my own life."

In 1957, the hotel was sold to the Augier family. Soon afterwards, Madame Jeanne Augier reinvigorated it with luxurious decorations and furnishings. I really loved this place. It had a unique style. Guests arriving at the hotel were immediately ushered into a sparkling lobby by a white-gloved doorman dressed in 19th century style. The hotel itself is an eclectic living museum in which 15th century antiques sit next to pieces of modern and contemporary art. Walking through the corridors and public areas, you can view original Salvador Dali paintings placed in proximity to ancient Japanese vases. Fantastic upholstered antique furniture is scattered around each landing. It is just a wonder!

In addition to this fabulous décor, the hotel has one of the finest restaurants in Nice, the Regency-styled Le Chanticleer, noted for its 18th century woodwork. The second restaurant in the hotel is Rotonde, a brasserie-style restaurant, that has the atmosphere of a carousel and a big English-style bar with walnut-wood paneling, velvet armchairs and portraits of the famous. The Hotel has hosted many famous guests—members of the Rockefeller and Vanderbilt families and the like.

As we drove along the sea on the coast, Helmut and Martin were gasping at the amazing beauty of the landscape. I wasn't surprised because I had felt that every day since I came here. We arrived at the Place du Casino at 3:30 p.m. As usual, I stopped in front of the Café de Paris and impressed my visitors with the fast appearance of the parking valets and their friendly service.

I had luck that day because Jeanette was working. She came up right away, said "Bon jour, Hansi" and gave me a kiss left and right on my cheeks. Given how impressed they were as they wound their way through the very expensive cars parked out front, my little personalized introduction just put the icing on the cake. For someone targeted to be busted and penniless, I sure was putting on a good show. She put some chocolate sprinkles on the icing when she seated us at an A plus table with a perfect view of the richly attired visitors to this extravagant restaurant.

A Simple Matter of Austrian Tax Law

*So what's going on? What's behind these
tax fraud charges?*

Gathering up his equipoise, Helmut handed me my home-town newspaper. The headlines said:

TAX AFFAIR: THE COURT WAITS FOR HANS SITTER

As President of his wife's company, Johann Sitter signed papers requesting money from the tax revenue office.

In Wiener Neustadt, the investigation of Sitter runs at full blast, but Johann Sitter has fled from authorities.

The search warrant initiated by the tax office in Wiener Neustadt claims that there was an illegal request for $1,500,000 of projected sales-tax money, followed by illegal handling of the money once it was received. Fearing that the accused might attempt flight, an arrest warrant was handed down immediately, but the accused managed to flee anyway.

It is possible that Sitter is not guilty, but he still would have to appear before the prosecutor for an interview in order to prove his innocence.

Sitter has escaped to Monaco, where he is now living.

I gasped out loud as I read the crazy article. *Unbelievable! What the hell is wrong with them? Why would I escape from something I knew nothing about? I am living in Monaco, perfectly legally, because that is my main residence! I cannot believe this shit. What a bunch of morons!*

Jeanette came by and I ordered us three Campari sodas and asked for the menu. After she brought the menu, Martin said, "The landscape is quite nice inside as well as along the coast. I understand why you like it here."

He paused, and Martin said, "So what's going on? What's behind these tax fraud charges? The talk on the street is that you split from Austria and took millions in tax revenue with you."

"Sorry, but that's bullshit. Be patient with me for a moment, because the situation is so stupid that it's a little difficult to explain.

"You see, back in 1994, I was working with Manfred Gass in Houston. He had developed a soda machine with a special design called the American Cooler. We obtained the patent rights for that machine and founded a company called Liberty, Inc.

"What was so unique about it?"

"It was basically the design. It had different colorful designs on the front—and the Statue of Liberty mounted on top. It looked a lot better than the average beverage dispenser in America.

"To raise money, I tried to find somebody for the worldwide distribution of the American Cooler. There was a company called Klimascheck Leasing owned by Erich Klimascheck. It was interested in distributing our machines along with the replaceable bags of syrup that would be part of the distribution deal.

"There were actually two parts to this deal. The first part is where my partner and I, Manfred Gass, formed our company, Liberty, Inc., retaining the rights to the design patent. I was President of this company, owning 50 percent of it and Manfred owning the other 50 percent. In the first part of the deal, Liberty, Inc. was going to sell the rights to worldwide distribution to Klimascheck whose main company was in Austria. He was to buy the worldwide rights for sales distribution of the American Cooler and its syrup for $20 million dollars from Liberty USA. Liberty, Inc. would retain its patent and production rights.

"Since he was buying these rights from an American company, in accordance with American law, he did not have to be concerned with sales tax.

"In the second part of the deal, my wife's company, Karisma, an Austrian company, was to buy the rights to five countries from Klimascheck for $7,500,000. These countries were Austria, Germany, Italy, France and Switzerland." I paused for a moment. The next part was hard to explain.

"I don't know, even though you are a reporter, how much you understand the way the Austrian government deals with sales tax, but it is very peculiar. When a retailer initiates a deal with a wholesaler, the wholesaler will actually bill the retailer for the taxes. He will then theoretically turn the taxes over to the government.

"So in the second part of this deal, when Karisma was purchasing the rights to actually distribute the American Cooler in five countries, it became the retailer, buying from the wholesaler. In this case, Karisma became the retailer who was billed for $1.5 million in taxes by Klimascheck, the wholesaler. The invoice looked something like this:

License and distribution rights
for American Cooler $7,500,000
20% Sales Tax   + $1,500,000
    $9,000,000

"The interesting thing about the Austrian system is that although the wholesaler was expected to pay the money to the Austrian government over a period of time, the retailer could ask for the entire amount back—to be put into an account from which the sales tax could be debited by the government right away.

"This is how it went down in our case. The sales tax was due quarterly, so for example, it might be due at the end of March, June, September and December. And Klimascheck was responsible for paying to the Austrian government the $1.5 million at the end of the quarter.

"In addition, Karisma, my wife's company, could actually ask the government to get from the tax agency a credit to its account by just filling out the form and sending the form and invoice to the agency with a signature. This was completely legal, even though the Austrian government had not yet received the funds, in whole or in part, from the wholesaler.

"But of course, in our case the deal hinged on Klimascheck coming up with the $20 million to pay to Liberty International. This was the money we would use to buy the rights from him and pay him the sales tax he would forward to the tax agency.

"Here's what happened. Klimascheck delivered the invoice to Karisma in April, at a time when I was not in Austria. My wife's bookkeeper filled out a form to request money from the government, which she signed and sent to the tax agency. We were then immediately given a $1.5 million credit by the agency in our bank account. This money, the $1.5 million, of course, needed to be provided by Klimascheck to the Austrian agency by the end of June.

"Hypothetically, someone in Karisma, including myself or my wife—or someone else in the company—could have taken the money out of the bank and headed for the hills. And since Klimascheck never paid the $20 million to us and the deal went south, naturally the government's money in our bank account could become a liability—and without a speedy resolution, it could look like someone was planning to abscond with it.

"So naturally when I came back and found out about what had happened, I consulted my CPA. As a result, the tax consultant for Karisma amended the sales tax declaration and explained to the Agency that the declaration claiming a credit of $1,500,000 had been incorrect. All the money was returned to the Agency. At the time the situation came to a head, I still owned the Hotel Freizeittempel.

"Two years later, ten people from the Revenue Office showed up at my apartment and searched my living quarters, the hotel and its office. Looking back today, from the sudden and omnivorous nature of the search and the fact that they didn't appear to find anything and that no one was arrested, I concluded this was more a tool for discovery than a legitimate search for a specific set of items—in other words, for some suspected sign of criminal activity.

"Since I was neither involved in issuing the invoice nor signing the application to the Revenue Office for the tax credit, why would they want to arrest me? By this time, I strongly suspected that someone with power connected to the Revenue service was deliberately trying to get me. But why?"

CHAPTER

16

Two Scandals for the Price of One!

At this point, I could virtually feel my bank account beginning to shrink.

I finished my explanations to Martin, who had been recording it while my lawyer made a lot of notes. Our food came as the late afternoon crowd began to flood into the Place du Casino. I began to see my two associates' eyes glaze over with the most common virus here—infatuation with the external trappings of wealth and fame, something I loved, to be sure, but also something that I had begun to see through. In fact, I saw something different than they did.

To my mind, now paralyzed with the threat of losing everything I had worked for, I began to see the restaurant patrons, as I did before, in another *Dia del Muerte* tableau. But this time, the macabre skeletal forms in designer wear and diamonds sparkled and glowed as they paraded all around us, casting splinters of light around the room, invisible to all except my own tortured eyes.

When we finished eating, I ordered a bottle of Beaujolais and my friends watched the sun set on the Place du Casino, but not me. I only had eyes for the richly attired guests whose sultry flesh was a micrometer away from rotten bones and the acrid stink of death.

When the sun had fully set, I suddenly snapped to. Regaining my composure and my normal vision, I signaled for Jeanette to bring the check and asked that the valet get the Bentley. I gave both of them a large tip but then began to have regrets. At this point, I could virtually feel my bank account beginning to shrink.

When we got to my apartment, I introduced Martin to Karin. Helmut, of course, knew her well. He and his wife had socialized with us for quite a few years. Deploying his usual charm and common sense, Helmut complimented my wife on her good looks—comments, I was sure, that would brighten the rest of her evening. After Martin took a couple of pictures for his paper, I asked Helmut to join me on the balcony to privately inform me as to what was going on with the money transfer and what the bank lady told me about Linkov. I could tell he was concerned because his eyes began to water as he spoke, "Your situation isn't very good, Hansi, not good at all."

THESE PETTY BUREAUCRATS, IN THE END, HAD ENORMOUS POWER OVER MY LIFE— AND SURVIVAL.

He continued, frowning slightly, "Not only are you involved in tax fraud with this $1.5 million with Karisma, in which you are a minor shareholder with only 1 percent of the company, but now you are involved in another scandal with Linkov, where you are poised to receive another $3 million for your hotel and your Beverly Hills Club from a crook who sold fake war bonds.

"They're thinking that you're always involved with crooks. One time it's Klimascheck, then it's Linkov and maybe some other criminals, and always with Johann Sitter's name in the middle of it. Look at things from the standpoint of a judge and prosecutors who think they are ten times smarter than you and get paid maybe two or three thousand a month.

"Every time your name comes up, it's about millions. Every official in Wiener Neustadt hates your guts. They're all jealous of your money and your lifestyle. And for Christ's sake, you know you've provoked them with your carrying on."

I looked down. Yes, I hated their petty little bureaucracy and how they used their puny powers to intimidate me. Helmut was right—I had definitely looked down at them as they tried to intimidate me with parking tickets, business licenses, stupid little health regulations and the like. I had been cocky and prideful, driving around their little town in my Bentley like I was the unrecognized King of the place. I now realized that, even if I was able to wiggle out of some of their little fines—so strange to me—and the intimidating over-regulation of hotel inspections and car registration, these petty bureaucrats, in the end, had enormous power over my life—and survival. I didn't think of that when I was driving around like that, because my life had hitherto been free of any accusations of criminality. I may have been a lot of things, but a criminal I was not.

Helmut noticed my distraction and put his hand on my shoulder. "None of this is any good, and the next news may be even worse. I'll try to get more info, but be careful about making light of this. There is nothing good on the horizon. It's all very bad."

I glanced in the window at Karin and my son in the other room. It wasn't just bad for me. Soon our whole world would go down. Helmut saw it all on my face.

"I'm sorry. As your lawyer, as well as your friend, I had to warn you. Let me go back to Austria now and see what I can do."

"Okay," I said. "Please say nothing about this to Karin while you're here. She's already more than nervous about the money transfer."

Helmut smiled, a bit grimly, I thought. "Don't worry," he said, "I won't say a word. Maybe we'll find a solution. Try being a little optimistic, in spite of what I've just said."

"You're kidding," I said. "If I wasn't able to be a little optimistic, I'd shoot myself right now."

17

A Resolution

"That's the reason why you have friends, stupid."

We went back into the apartment. I poured out a glass of cognac for everyone, attempting to make light conversation with Karin. Philipp got a bit restless; I watched him happily hopping around. His sheer joy in being with us triggered a sudden apprehension in me, since where we lived and everything we did was resting on a thin sliver of happenstance—would various Austrian officials somehow change their minds, and would I retrieve my three million dollars.

I began to feel tiny beads of sweat forming on my forehead. Despite everything, I tried to be funny and charming. I noticed it was getting to be 9:00 p.m.

I interrupted the conversation to say, "You know, we have only this one night left, and I really want you to meet my good friend Gerhard." I told them how Gerhard had escaped from the Vienna Boys' Choir to join the French Foreign Legion when he was seventeen. They thought it was crazy but extremely amusing—I suspect both of them thought I was making it up.

"Well, you can meet him and decide for yourself," I said, motioning for them to come with me. I gave Philly and Karin a kiss and said goodbye to Umberto, who looked offended because I wasn't taking him with me.

Within minutes we had crossed the plaza and were at Gerhard's Café. Roberto and Angelique were both working. The atmosphere was great, and the place was bubbling over with happy people talking a jillion languages. Gerhard's Café was full of regulars—almost everyone knew everyone else.

Gerhard came up to me and gave me a big hug. I introduced Helmut and Martin to him. Without further ado, he ordered us a bottle of Veuve Cliquot Champagne and the café's special appetizer, Champagne Scietre Caviar on little buns. He then sat down with us on the terrace and, for the next two hours, regaled us with his stories and hospitality.

For me Gerhard was like a tranquillizer, a human being endowed with the almost magical properties to help me forget my worries and, whatever my state of mind, to experience my natural joy of life again.

It was close to midnight when Gerhard decided to take us to Jimmy'z, the famous Cote D'Azur nightclub for the rich and famous. Like the Café de Paris, it is the place to see and be seen. I'm afraid to say that once you have visited Jimmy'z, all other clubs lose some of their grandeur. I knew how pricey their drinks were, so I was happy to accept Gerhard's invitation.

We took his Peugeot to Jimmy'z, nestled in a small corner by the Mediterranean on the beach by the Avenue Princess Grace in Monte Carlo, maybe a mile away from Gerhard's Café. The entrance to Jimmy'z is quite dramatic. The hedges and palm trees were all lit up gloriously, beautifully encircled by a dark sky filled with blazing stars and the restless sea. It was a gorgeous night, the perfect chance to sit in the open-air section of the club, where the ceiling is composed of those millions of real stars shedding their light on the rich and famous, the wealthy wannabees and those whose destiny might be somewhere in between, or out of the box altogether.

It was now close to one o'clock in the morning, and Jimmy'z, a Mecca for late-night bloomers, slowly began to get busy. But that wasn't any excuse for ignoring Gerhard and his guests when we arrived. In fact, for all practical purposes, there might as well had been a spotlight on us when we entered the room. Everyone on the door greeted Gerhard with great affection, and for the remainder of the evening we were all treated like royalty.

For a club, Jimmy'z is huge, with lots of seating areas, both inside and outside, and a great dance floor. The music that night had some kind of Latino beat—I think it was Brazilian. I couldn't make out the lyrics at all, but it seemed like it was a mélange of very heavy, somber love songs. Most of the time the dancing was very deliberate, very slow—and most of the musicians seemed to be frowning, but the gaiety and laughter of the guests rose above the somber atmosphere.

We couldn't help but gawk at the insanely beautiful women in that club tonight, each of them looking like a model from *Cosmopolitan*. The dazzling little waterfalls sprinkled with the colored tapestry of lights from the dance floor added another layer of joyfulness to drown out the slow, methodical clicking of maracas and the deep, unrelenting notes of the bass guitar.

As the evening progressed, Gerhard plied us with champagne and exotic tropical drinks. It was filled with witticisms, local gossip and fabulous stories. Slowly, I began to twinge with guilt. In my penurious state, the money that he pulled out of his wallet seemed an extraordinary act of beneficence for me and filled me with apprehension about my immediate future. As drink after drink arrived at our table, I began to feel terrible. How much money was he spending on my behalf? It was stupid, I know, but I began to think of myself as a parasite.

We didn't leave till 4 a.m. Gerhard drove us to my yacht, where my visitors and I would spend the night. When we said goodbye, I said, "Why did you do that? My friendship is becoming way too expensive. That night on the town must have cost you seven or eight hundred bucks!"

Gerhard looked at me as though I had lost my mind. "Shut up, Hansi," he said. "Are you forgetting how often you paid when things were going your way? Don't look at my tiny little gift that way." Then he struck me hard but playfully on the shoulder. "That's the reason why you have friends, stupid." He smiled. "Don't worry, I'm fine," he said, giving me a hug and leaving, after nodding goodbye to all of us.

After putting Helmut and Martin to bed on the yacht, I found that, despite it being early morning, I was still restless. I poured myself a cognac and a glass of water, took out a choice cigar, a relic of my more extravagant days, and sat down on my aft deck. I looked at the sky's tapestry of stars and thought of the dancing lights of the ballroom and the grandeur of the last few hours. I looked around the harbor and up at the castle at the rock cliff jutting upwards. This was home, damn it! This was my *home!*

With every puff of that expensive cigar, I got more melancholic, the cognac no doubt accelerating the depression. Involuntarily, tears came into my eyes as I thought how close I had been, with that three million dollars of hard-earned money, to a great life.

I HAVE A RENDEZVOUS WITH YOU, MONACO ...

Why was all this happening to me? After about a half an hour of depressive drama, I became sleepy. Yet I didn't want to go to bed in this state. I guess I felt that strange, compelling sense of determination—when life seems to demand that you either throw in the towel or jump out a window, and you know you must refuse.

I might have to leave, but no power on Earth could make me doubt that, in some profound way, I had an almost mystical tie to this place, something I did not want to ever give up. So I looked around at the little port of Fontvieille and swore that if I left Monaco now, I would come back. I would come back with my dignity re-established, some money in my pocket and my friendships here still intact. *I have a rendezvous with you, Monaco*, I said. Satisfied at the strength of my resolution, I finally staggered off to bed.

18

Karin

*I had begun to embark on Plan B, a plan of action if
I failed to reconcile with the Austrian government.*

I woke up at 11 a.m., went down to Helmut and Martin's cabin
and saw that they were both still sleeping. Saying goodbye to
them was hard, but frankly I was exhausted from all our partying
and I was glad to get back to my little family. I took the Basse
Corniche road towards the Nice airport so they could enjoy the
last view of the coast.

About fifteen miles before the airport, I stopped over at the
Rotonde Brasserie in the Hotel Negresco, where they could also
enjoy a nice view of the beach. To avoid the high cost of valet
parking, I hunted for a nearby parking area. This would be the
first of many lifestyle concessions I was about to make to forestall
the complete draining of my bank account. After this day, every
purchase, every expense would be measured.

Last night's binge had left me with a dire thirst for beer, so I ordered Peroni, an Italian beer, to go along with our preserved pigeon legs on a bed of crispy lettuce, a lovely dish with a formidable name, which I ordered for all three of us. We all enjoyed nursing our hangovers with the beer—we were quite tired after the festivities at Jimmy'z.

At the airport they both promised me many times that they would try to help me resolve my problems as soon as possible. It wasn't that I didn't believe them, but I had begun to embark on Plan B, a plan of action if I failed to reconcile with the Austrian government.

On the way home, I stopped in Eze, where I bought some roses from a cute little flower cart on the side of the road. I was tired but thrilled when I finally parked my Bentley in the garage. I walked into the apartment, quickly putting the roses in a vase, and was about to look for Karin and Philipp when the phone rang. It was Karin.

"Hi, Baby, where are you?" I detected a strange tone in her voice with her response. She said, "Martha came by with Andrew and we took the kids to the playground in the park."

Martha was a good friend of ours. Gerhard had introduced us. Originally she had worked with Gerhard on a number of yachts—she had worked in the kitchen while he worked as a sailor. She hailed from Styria, a part of Austria that Arnold Schwarzenegger, our most famous Austrian, had once called home. Her son Andrew's father was a black guy from Jamaica, the third member on the yacht where they had all met. Andrew was a year older than Philipp, but they got along pretty well. Happily, Martha would sometimes care for Philipp when Karin and I enjoyed a night on the town. I really liked Martha and was happy that my son had the opportunity to talk to someone his age in German.

When Karin finished her explanation, I could sense something very nasty in her voice. I said, "Okay, that's fine. You're mad. I've been too busy entertaining our guests. But I understand. Will you come back now?"

"After we take the kids to eat at McDonald's," she said.

She seemed to be calming down. Maybe it was the thought of going to McDonald's that calmed her. It's hard to believe, but McDonald's was a big treat for the locals, a practical way to save money for the foolish middle class brave enough to try and make do here, and a novelty for the super-rich, who liked to go slumming from time to time. Then, of course, there were the tourists, who needed a break from the big, expensive restaurants.

I never thought a McDonald's would be successful in Monaco, but I was wrong. McDonald's was located exactly at the entrance to the port in Fontvieille. It was two floors high next to a shopping center and was crowded day and night with tourists as well as locals who also bowed their head to eat at the world's most popular junk-food trough.

"Well, have a big Mac on me," I said semi-humorously, still not liking her tone. "I'm going to hit the sack early. I'm tired as hell."

I remember that she didn't call me "Dear" or "Baby" in that parting goodnight call. I turned the TV on and fell into a deep sleep immediately, so deep I didn't hear Karin, Philly and Umberto enter the apartment. When I woke up, everyone was in bed.

SOMETHING WAS GOING ON AND I DIDN'T KNOW WHAT IT WAS.

The next morning started as usual, transporting Philipp to kindergarten. Weird vibes were coming from Karin, and acting on my intuition, I tried to stay away from her as much as possible. Not knowing what to think but knowing she was probably displeased with me, I wanted to avoid any kind of confrontation or fight. Something was going on and I didn't know what it was. After breakfast at Gerhard's, I was ready for a little exercise to chase my problems away, at least momentarily. Later that afternoon I would probably hear from Helmut, for better or worse. If things were unresolved, I would again spend a long, long weekend with nothing to do but wait and play at being happy.

Returning, I was relieved to find that Karin had already left, and I didn't have to face any probing questions about when the final transfer of the money would come through. I put on shorts, a shirt and running shoes and got ready to jog along the shore.

Heading towards the Mala Footpath, a two-mile-long coastal path that extends from Plage Marquet (Marquet Beach) west from Fontvieille along the coastline to the Port of Cap d'Ailand and the splendid Plage de Mala was my destination. It's a wonderful run when the sea is calm, but in a rough sea you were in danger of being washed away. In the summertime there is not much shade, so the path gets very hot.

Further along it, as you leave behind the concrete walls of Monaco and the Port of Cap d'Ail, the vegetation suddenly turns wild and you follow a succession of rocky coves and bays. Finally you pass underneath the exquisite Belle Epoque villas, where you can only imagine the sumptuous views enjoyed by the occupants.

This is a magical route, with plenty of intriguing little detours and accessible coves that shelter secluded areas to swim in. The last bend round the cape and a beautiful but strenuous staircase bring you to what I believe to be the most mysterious and gorgeous beach on the Cote d'Azur. This is a lot to say. The Cote d'Azur has a lot of beautiful bays, but La Mala is unbeatable.

I went along that path many, many times, sometimes jogging alone as I did that morning, but also with my family. Philipp loved to climb a bit away from the path and explore the little caves. I loved that little path, and one day, the last moment when I am on earth, I hope that the last picture I will take with me— to the next universe or eternity—will be of me playing with Philipp at that beach at La Mala.

Ultimately I wound up at the little restaurant I had visited with Gerhard a couple of days ago, but with the yacht when we anchored in the bay and a dinghy had picked us up. I saw the yachts anchored in the bay, and it looked, as usual, peaceful and gorgeous. Money may not be everything, but one thing I know: people with money know exactly where to go and spend it, to beautiful places like this amazing bay.

It was close to lunchtime when I sat down to eat at a little outside table, ordering a shrimp salad and water. After eating, I went closer to the water and lay down in a beach chair beside a row of beautiful ladies, mostly topless, and a few amorous couples. It was naptime for most of us, eager to rest in the warm sun and perhaps get a slightly better tan. The beach chairs with their colorful umbrellas, positioned directly in front of the restaurant, created a colorful, inviting ambiance.

I woke to my cell phone ringing and wriggling slightly on the blanket beneath me. Still dizzy from my nap, I picked up the phone and found Helmut on the line. I felt my spine straightening up as I greeted him, waiting tensely to hear his report. "Hi Hans! How are you doing?" he said.

"Hopefully better, after I talk to you and hear your great news."

It almost seemed like the phone went dead for a moment, then Helmut's voice spoke to me very gravely: "I'm

"HERR LINKOV IS UNDER ARREST, AND ALL HIS ACCOUNTS ARE FROZEN."

sorry, Hans, but I don't have good news to report. In fact, in many respects, it is quite the opposite."

I covered the phone and took a deep breath. He continued. "First of all, I had a long talk with the judge and despite my objections and, I believe, incisive arguments, he refused to cancel the arrest warrant. Secondly, I went over to the bank and they claim they can do nothing to re-open the account and send you the money.

"Herr Linkov is under arrest, and all his accounts are frozen. Judging from the report the bank sent me, he sold fake war bonds, collecting more than $20 million from unwary investors, and was trying to get another $100 million from the Brazilian government. It will be a long time before you can even have a shot at getting your money back, probably sometime after Linkov's prosecution.

"Even then, there would most likely have to be a court case, and the Revenue Office in Austria will fight you anyway to make you pay tax on the transfer. Even though you're legally entitled to receive that money tax-free in Monaco, the Austrian government would probably keep you in court for years, forcing you to spend every last cent that you had."

Stunned and speechless, my body slumped back in the chair as if paralyzed. Without even realizing it, I had dropped the cell phone onto the blanket. Although my body was lifeless, it was as if there was a tornado in my head, setting off millions of tiny piercing neurological signals, igniting a monster migraine somewhere behind my eyes. Even now I cannot describe the horribly self-destructive thoughts that whirled around in my head. Later, revenge would rule my consciousness, but now I could only think of doing harm to myself.

CHAPTER

19

Confession

*I had passed through this portal of failure before and
now I must take everything to a new level.*

Frrom the cell phone on the blanket, I heard Helmut's voice
coming from a million miles away. Suddenly I came back to life
and picked up the phone, "Hans, Hans, are you still there?"

"Fuck, yes, I'm here."

Poised in between the world of paralyzing pain and some
kind of mental hibernation, I was having trouble thinking clearly.
When those moments passed, my first thought was, *Please let me
die right now and bury me under a beautiful tree near my favorite
cave on the Mala Footpath. Let me die right now.* But, then, in a
split second, I saw my favorite companion in life bending over
my grave ... my beautiful little son with that warm, innocent
smile, whose life would be destroyed by my capitulation to the
sweet escape of death.

I came to life again, my self-destructive thoughts now giving way to the first rush of violent anger. In these terrible moments, I thought of going back to Austria and shooting Linkov and all those who wanted to arrest me. But as these thoughts flew through my mind, I knew they were bogus and dangerous, so I cancelled them as fast as I could. I heard myself saying to Helmut in words that seemed to take minutes to get out, "What should I do now?"

Well, even though I dearly loved my friend Helmut, he was a lawyer after all, and so his first bit of advice should surely not have come as a shock. Speaking quite clearly, he said, "The first thing we have to do is fight the arrest warrant. Now, believe me, it's going to be tough, so I will ask you to send me money—I'll tell you how much I need in a couple of days. After we fix that problem, we can go from there."

Although I said nothing, my twisted, angry self spoke quite loudly in my head. "*FUCK IT!*" it said. In a moment or two, my still reasonably sane and diplomatic self said out loud, but in slow motion, "Let me think about it and I'll get in touch."

He then said, shrewdly attempting to consolidate his money request, "Hey, I filed an appeal against the arrest warrant already and sent it to the court. I'll send you a copy."

Feeling like taking the phone and throwing it into the sea, I managed to calm myself, saying "Thank you, Helmut" with as much grace as I could muster, all the while screaming *FUCK IT!* in my mind.

Now I knew my inevitable destiny—to see all my dreams washed away in this incredible fairytale kingdom, while all my start-up capital dissolved away before I could make my happily anticipated journey to the New World.

Then a new thought rippled through me like a master archer's arrow aimed precisely at the center of my heart: *KARIN—Oh, my God, what can I tell Karin?* Even with the expected $3 million in hand, she was not at all happy with the prospect of leaving Monaco. Going with no money to a strange country where we would start off from scratch would surely not thrill her at all.

I paid for my meager lunch and started to walk back. Embroiled in silent horror, I was oblivious to the beauty around me. It took a long time to walk home, and for most of that time I was in some strange altered state. Despite losing touch with the world around me, I managed to cobble together a plan to break the truth to Karin.

I decided that the best idea would be to have Martha come to our apartment with Andrew and take the kids off our hands for the night. I would take Karin out to dinner and explain everything to her, honestly, reasonably and with as much optimism as I could muster under the circumstances.

And I would tell her how much I loved her, and how, over the years, I had shown her my resilience in some of the worst financial scrapes she had ever seen. I would promise, despite any trepidation that I had at that moment, that I would again rebuild our lives—that I loved her—that I would do it to take her to even higher levels—that she would soon see the fruits of my resolve. Yes, that's what I would do.

Even as I devised this plan I was full of anxiety, but I also knew that in some sense I had passed through this portal of failure before and now I must take everything to a new level. And, as I thought of telling Karin my resolution, I knew that I had to make it true within myself. This was a challenge I would have to face so that I could make that rendezvous in Monaco that I had promised myself on my yacht last night.

As I renewed these promises to myself, I walked more briskly, gradually rediscovering the world around me. Nearing Fontvieille, I decided to head over to Gerhard's first to check with him about my plan of action.

I was lucky. He was there and not exceptionally busy, and he greeted me pleasantly. Angelique brought us two glasses of Pinot Grigio and we went outside.

> "LISTEN TO ME, HANSI; KEEP YOUR COOL."

Gerhard listened carefully to the entire story, was silent for a while, and finally said, "I really wouldn't like to be in your shoes right now. But try and remember, there is always a way out—the right way out—so don't do anything stupid." He leaned across the table and jabbed my shoulder with his index finger, "Listen to me, Hansi, keep your cool. We'll find a way, I promise you ... I'll do anything I can do to help you, but please don't give up on yourself."

"What about Karin?"

"Yes, I think it's a good plan—go take Karin somewhere, somewhere pleasant. Take your time, have a nice dinner. Let me call Martha now to make sure she can take care of the kids." With his call, Martha was off to the apartment in 20 minutes. She was there when I arrived, and Karin already knew that I was taking her out to dinner. Quickly moving to the bedroom, I threw on an acceptable jacket.

As I walked out of the bedroom, Umberto and Philly both jumped on me with Philly crying out, "Daddy, and Daddy— you're here!" It almost broke my heart to realize how quickly my son's future had fallen into profound uncertainty and how sadly his fate would be tied to mine, no matter what I did. Karin noticed my sudden mood swing but gave me a kiss anyway and said, "What's happened? Is something wrong? What's with this sudden dinner?"

"Martha's here," I said. "She'll cook something nice for the kids and we'll go somewhere for dinner and I'll explain what's going on." Karin was smart—she had caught on that this was not an ordinary something. "Tell me right now," she said.

"Baby, please—this isn't that simple. I need more time to tell you." I'm ashamed to say that I then flat-out lied to her. "It's no big deal, believe me—nothing all that bad, but we do need to talk."

She gave me a strange look as if she didn't believe me and said, "Fine. Why not? I'm hungry, anyway."

As we went down the elevator, I tried to smile and asked: "Okay, are you ready for a nice evening?"

"We'll see," she said, very flatly in a voice that I had not heard before.

CHAPTER

20

A Fateful Confrontation

"For better or for worse," I mumbled to myself inaudibly.

Was this my imagination, a bit of paranoia sneaking in the backdoor of my already besieged subconscious? *She sees right through me. She knows I'm lying*, I thought. And there was that indefinable something about her demeanor that I couldn't really place. Was it just suspicion—or some type of cold contempt?

I buried these speculations quickly, knowing my only safety net was my own sense of security, my own ability to meet any challenge headlong. I needed to concentrate on the night before me, on unraveling what had happened in the right way and in a way that she could somehow find comforting.

We took the Range Rover. As we pulled out of the garage, I asked her, "What do you think about Eze? It's not really that far and we can talk on the way over there."

"Yes, that's fine with me," she said, quickly looking out her window as we headed towards the small road that wound up the mountains with the Chateau de la Chevre d'or as our destination. Once there, we would walk through the little narrow path in the castle between the walls, hand in hand, and find our hearts joined together, despite the adversity. "For better or for worse," I mumbled to myself inaudibly.

"What?" she said sharply, without turning her head from her window.

"Nothing," I said, steeling myself to concentrate on that narrow steep road. I began to drive very slowly, hoping I could safely navigate that way and still begin the dreadful conversation that I had forestalled for so long. "Listen, Karin, I want you to listen to what I have to say before you make any kind of judgment. Agreed?"

"Yes," she said, still looking out of her window. She had not glanced my way once since we had left the apartment. Riding in the car like that, with her head pointed out her window, made everything harder. Did she know already—and was she so angry that she wouldn't look at me? Nonetheless, I began to awkwardly spill the guts of my sad story. "Things have not worked out for us, Karin. I'm going to need your help and love to get through this."

She didn't say anything for at least two minutes. "What are you trying to tell me? Try and say something that makes some kind of sense."

"We're going to have to be strong for Philipp."

"Strong for Philipp? Why? What are you talking about?"

HOW IN THE HELL COULD I KNOW HE WAS SELLING PHONY WAR BONDS?

"For survival," I stumbled. "So we can survive."

"I'm not going to listen to one more word of this, Hans, unless you flat-out tell me what's wrong and stop this moaning and stupidity."

"The money is not coming. Linkov was indicted for selling phony war bonds and the government froze his account."

She shook her head. "What does that mean? Didn't you tell me that he has the money and nobody could stop the transfer? You told me you sold him everything. He moved in already. Tell me you're kidding!"

"No, Karin, I'm not kidding. How in the hell could I know he was selling phony war bonds? Tell me? How could I know?"

"I can't answer that, Hans. You're the smart guy, remember? You told me—when I asked you—'It's a done deal, baby!' What is done now, my sweet smart husband? We've lost everything! Great deal, Hansi!" There it was again. The icy contempt.

"You know we were losing money every month. I showed you in black-and-white. I saw our chance with Linkov—we could get rid of everything and start over. I took the chance and was close to getting it done. What you don't get is that I had really, really bad luck."

"Bad luck? Give me a break! You're a special kind of gambler— you know that. You never stop operating on the edge. I was against selling it, 100 percent. And now look, we have nothing. Nothing!"

Then why all this contempt? I thought you loved me, I said to myself. "So what does Helmut say about all this?"

"He wants me to send him money so he can continue to fight the warrant."

I paused. Although it was true, her manner was affecting me. It was like she was driving nails into me—one sentence at a time. I tried to say something positive. "The only solution is to take whatever we can and get over to America, like we were planning to anyway. I think I can rebuild everything—even our lifestyle. I think I can get us back here—eventually."

"With no money, with no business? You are truly a Fantasy Man, Hansi."

"We can do it."

Now, after all that contemptuous exchange, she suddenly became quiet. By this time, I was pretty close to the top of the mountain, about 1,800 feet up from sea level. Mechanically I glanced at the protective railing on the side of the road, designed to keep cars from falling down the steep rock wall to our left.

Even in the midst of our conversation, I watched for cars coming from the other direction. When they came, I slowed down and drove carefully by so that I didn't veer into one or somehow knock it over the railing. All this was clearly possible. I didn't want to die like Grace Kelly in a car accident here on this beautiful but dangerous scenic road.

After a few minutes more of our long and heavy silence, Karin said, "You know, maybe you're broke and you need to run over to the U.S., but I sure as hell don't. Not me. I don't need to."

"Oh," I said sarcastically, "you have an independent income and a lot of money to stay here. This is Monaco. If I'm the Fantasy Man, you're the Fantasy Woman."

For the first time, she looked at me and smiled. "I already have my insurance plan. It's already bought and paid for. So you don't need to worry about me."

For the first time, I was truly baffled and said, "Stop smiling!"

She turned away and looked out her window. "How can I help it? You're such a fool."

With one hand, I grabbed her by the shoulder, pulling her over to me while the car nearly veered into the railing. The brakes screeched as I said roughly, "What the hell are you talking about? Do you think you're smarter than me?"

"Way smarter," she said, trying to shake me off. "Get your hands off me and drive the fucking car."

I let her go for a moment, but I was beginning to get angry and my hands were shaking. She turned to me again and put a hand on mine. It was not a comforting hand—she was just trying to keep my hand steady on the wheel so we could navigate the mountain. "Watch what you're doing."

"I don't like what you're saying."

"I don't care. All you need to know is that I don't give a damn if you want to run away or not. I am going to stay here—because I can and I want to. You can do whatever is in your sick head to do. Just don't count on me to go along with it anymore."

She looked me in the face and grinned even harder. I yanked my hand off the wheel and pushed her away. The car swerved again, but I recovered control. She still looked at me, her smile mocking me. Now I had become enraged. I was losing control. I wanted to wipe that damn smile off her face with the back of my hand, but I knew I should restrain myself.

Where was she going with all this? "I told you before. Wipe that fucking smile off your face!"

21

The Revelation!

*I leapt out of the car, ran over to her side and
dragged her out the door of the car.*

Although she surely could see the anger boiling up in me, she ignored my warning. That was perhaps the biggest mistake she ever made—because that smug little smile was like someone pouring gasoline on a fire. What did she think? Why was she doing this? I turned towards her.

"What are you talking about, Karin? Tell me what the fuck you're talking about."

Now, for a moment, she stopped smiling. "Look, I'm already with your friend Walter."

"What are you talking about ... with my friend Walter?"

"You know exactly what I mean. And I can tell you right now, he is more than happy to take care of me and Philipp and ..."

Time suddenly sped up as my blood boiled over. Karin hadn't even finished her sentence when I instinctively veered sharply to the left into a little scenic parking area. Everything that was about to transpire no doubt happened in seconds, but my rage and anguish turned the world into a slow-motion inferno of anger.

I turned too fast and nearly ran through the railing. Catching my recklessness just in time, I jumped on the brakes, glancing over and seeing Karin's body thrust suddenly forward, her head just missing crashing into the windshield.

Oblivious to her discomfort, terror or contempt, I leapt out of the car, ran over to her side and dragged her out the door of the car. I pulled her over to the railing. With one hand on her throat and one securely gripping her hair in a death lock, I bent her shaking body over the railing.

The moon had risen. You could hear the crashing of the waves. It was bright enough to see the straight 1,500-foot drop to the brutal rocks below. As I held her over the railing, I felt a strange calm come over me.

I talked intently, but very quietly, "Listen, you rotten bitch. When you tell me you are fucking my friend, probably in my own bed—you and the other person in my life I trusted with my whole heart—that's bad enough. "But when you tell me that this stupid bastard is now going to take care of my son—and you say it with a mischievous laugh and a smile—then after all these years, you have never remotely understood who I am and what I am capable of."

She was now shaking so hard that I had to tighten my grip to keep her from shaking loose and tumbling to her death below. "Walter's a treacherous little asshole and you are a disgusting little whore, fucking someone I let in my house and treated like the brother he pretended to be. And now you laugh and smile and tell me this piece of shit is going to take my place. You think that's funny?" I shouted, tightening my grip on her throat.

She tried to shake her head but could barely move it. I leered at her. "Go ahead. Smile, bitch," I said.

She tried again to shake her head "no," but again could barely move it. Still I could feel the pressure of her desperate attempt. "Smile once now, and it'll be your ticket to the next world. I swear to God I will end your miserable life right here and now. Never, never laugh in my face again and tell me that some asshole will take care of my son."

Her eyes glistened with fear. There was not a trace of humor in them. "That freaking asshole you sleep with got all his money from an inheritance—$300,000 from his grandfather and then another $250,000 after an uncle died, then more money and a house from some other stupid relative. That is your pitiful lover's track record. He is a teacher. With his salary alone, you would not give a shit about him. So if that's your insurance policy, I hope he is goddamn careful with his money."

I was getting louder. "That's Walter's success record, but who gives a shit? Now to you, bitch. I am giving you one last crack at survival. For the sake of our son, who may love you even after he finds out who you really are, I may spare your life. But only, bitch, if I hear you apologize to me. This is your only chance. You have ten seconds ...."

I slowly released my grip and let her stand upright. But although she tried to talk, nothing would come out of her mouth, as desperate as she was. She fell down to the ground, kneeling before me, tears pouring out of her eyes.

EVEN IN MY MOST PERVERSE STATE OF ANGER, I ALMOST FELT SORRY FOR HER.

After about a minute, I heard a raw, sore voice croak out, "I'm sorry, Hansi. I'm really sorry." I took the side of my foot and pushed her over on the ground. She lay there, shaking ... her face turned white, snow-white, and for a moment she looked like she might pass out. But just when I thought she was no longer conscious, she began to crawl towards me. Her face was crisscrossed with stripes where her tears had streaked her makeup. She looked eerie in the moonlight; she looked like a ghost. When she reached me, she curled beneath my feet. Having begun her apology, she couldn't stop crying and stuttering: "I'm sorry, I'm so sorry ...!"

I looked down at her. She now just seemed like a hurt little child. Even in my most perverse state of anger, I almost felt sorry for her. Yet at the same time I wanted to do something more than scare her—I wanted to trash both her and the traitorous Walter together, to pound them into some kind of bloody oblivion.

In the back of my mind, I knew then—as I do now—that I had let my animal self out of its cage, that I was not handling this as a complete or whole human being. With their knives twisting in my heart, I had gone beyond the breaking point. Should I go any further?

In so much pain now—and perhaps stricken with pangs of conscience as I saw the writhing little wild animal I had turned my wife into, a wretched fox caught in a steel trap—I wondered if I should just drag her to the railing and pull her off with me, both of us tumbling down to our deaths, our bodies smashed and broken on the jagged edges of the rocks and our souls united forever.

I had descended so deeply that I had lost my moral compass, but although everything seemed to lose its clarity around me, I realized at that moment how close that pitiful white ghost crawling beneath me had come to her final moments. I prayed for a respite from this overwhelming desire to crush and destroy.

Gripped now by some strange objectivity, I helped Karin up and pulled her away from the railing towards the car. I then let her hand go. She fell down onto the grass, tears still streaming down her face. She was wailing now—in terror, but I am quite sure without remorse. I imagine she was in a state of shock, realizing that I was in such a state of rage and surprise that I might indeed have pushed her off a cliff. I looked down at her, now pitiless—and said, "Shut up and stop crying. Get your ass in the car. Now!"

She complied immediately. She continued to weep quietly for a while, and then became silent. In that deadly silence, I began to reflect on the feelings I had had for well over a year from time to time, culminating with her strange smiles and callousness as I unfolded to her the terrible financial drama that had robbed us of our future. It was hard to believe. And now Walter!

CHAPTER

22

Walter

*Please, Hans, don't do this. Don't expel me
from your life—"*

Less than eight weeks ago, I confronted Walter in a not so nice way. This happened back in the *Freizeittempel*, where he had become an ever-present reality in my life. Despite the fact that I liked him, his hovering omnipresence was getting under my skin.

He would come to the hotel almost every weekend, always looking for me and generally going to my apartment when he didn't find me. When I went to my apartment for any reason, he was always there, talking to Karin.

One Saturday morning, I found him there. He wasn't really alone because I could hear Karin out in the kitchen. He was reading in an armchair when I walked in. He started to get up.

"No, don't get up. Please." He sat down, puzzled at my tone. "You know, you're with us every weekend now," I said, surprising myself with the abruptness and bluntness of my observations.

"No matter what I do, where I go, it's always me, Karin and you. I believe that a lot of people are talking about us, even wondering if we are some kind of weird triangle and having sex together."

I had already faced a similar situation with my first wife, Herti, and I didn't want to get into another scene like that with Karin. Didn't I have any other types of friends besides the kind who would cheat with a friend's wife? Good God!

"Hans—" he started to reply.

"Tell me, my friend, is this really because of Karin—or are you in love with me?" Walter looked at me like I was crazy. "Because I'm only interested in women," I continued cruelly, "particularly in my wife."

"How can you ... ?"

"Shut up. So you're not queer?"

"No."

"I have nothing against gays. I just don't want them ..."

"I'm not queer, Hans. For God's sake ..."

"Well, then, is it Karin—?" He looked at me as though I were crazy. "I'm going to ask you a question, Walter. And you better answer me correctly—without any bullshit .... " He looked at me. "Are you fucking Karin?"

Now Walter's face turned ashen. I actually saw tears in his eyes. "I can't believe you're talking like this to me. I thought you knew me. Why are you bringing all this strangeness into something so simple?"

"Simple. What's so simple?"

"It's called friendship, Hansi." He took some deep breaths as his eyes watered up. "I'm amazed you could ever think this about me. I thought you believed I was your friend, maybe one of your best friends."

I looked at those tears and his red face, listening to the softness of his words, and I began to doubt my suspicions. My anger rapidly began to fade.

"How could you think that I would ever do that to you? My God, I never would do that to you—or any other friend of mine—ever, whatever happened."

Walter was ten years older than me. I didn't think he was particularly handsome—I only perceived him as a threat because of his weirdly encroaching proximity to me during every free hour I had. "Look, I'm beginning to believe you," I said.

"You should, Hansi. You really should."

I now believed that he was telling the truth—but still, I felt intruded on. "Maybe so. But I'm going to be honest with you. Maybe it's irrational, maybe it's my territorial instinct, but I don't want you around all the time. I want to be with Karin alone."

"I understand. If I had known I was intruding, I would have gotten out of your hair a long time ago."

I relented and put my arm on his shoulder. He was slumped down in

"**WHAT'S GOING ON HERE, HANSI? WHAT ARE YOU DOING TO WALTER?**"

the chair. Although my touch was meant to console him, my words were meant to create the space I needed—and, perhaps, given his little speech and sincerely spoken promise, a bit harsh. "Walter, I want you to call before you come here. Call me. And I want you to give me space to be alone with Karin over the weekends."

He got up slowly, suddenly looking as if he had aged several years. He walked to the door, and then turned around. I couldn't believe it. I was forty-three years old and Karin was thirty, and this older man—now fifty-three—had knelt down on my living room floor, torrents of tears pouring out of his eyes, saying, "Please, Hans, don't do this. Don't expel me from your life—"

"I didn't say—"

"I know what you're doing. You're pushing me away ..."

At this point Karin, hearing all the fracas, came rushing in. She was alarmed to see Walter in this state. Not knowing what had happened, she knelt down beside him, putting her arm around his shoulder as if consoling a child who had fallen off a bicycle. She looked at me accusingly. "What's going on here, Hansi? What are you doing to Walter?"

Walter ignored her completely. He looked me straight in the eyes and simply begged, "Please, please, Hans—don't do that to me! I don't have any friends besides you. I don't have any family. I spend all my extra time taking care of a sick mother who almost doesn't know who I am." Karin looked at him with total compassion and glared at me. I was embarrassed for him more than anything. Perhaps I had too much testosterone for my own good—too little compassion, too little humanity—or perhaps, as I think now, my psychic functions had gone into overdrive.

He still managed to go on. "Remember Roberta, my girlfriend who I broke up with a year ago? I guess you think I forgot her ..." he continued, blurting out with almost angry indignation, "and replaced her WITH YOUR WIFE?"

"I love Roberta. I think of her every day. No one can replace her," he said, looking at Karin for the first time, with grim determination on his face—as if to say: *Look how Hansi is wronging me. How could he possibly think I have fallen for you?* "No, Hansi, you guys have become everything to me. You're my friends, you're my family. I need you and your friendship. Please!"

I stared at him, almost shocked by my lack of sympathy, even as my wife looked up to me with pleading, almond eyes and I saw that the front of his shirt and even his collar were wet with tears. "All right," I said unfeelingly. "I'll let you visit over the weekends. But even so, I want space. Can you handle that?"

He nodded. "I'll go now and come back later."

"Take your time," I said. "Maybe late this afternoon you can drop by and we can have a drink."

"Okay," he said and left.

Karin stayed on the floor, looking at me. "How could you treat him like that? And what were you thinking about me?"

No matter how he felt or how I forgave him, I thought he acted like a freaking asshole. But I didn't say that to Karin.

CHAPTER

23

Despair

Tilt! I had never felt anything like this before.

Driving back from the mountaintop with my wife weeping silently beside me, all I could think of was that mendacious episode, so filled with lies and distortions. If nothing else, they both were outrageous actors. But I didn't want them in my movie anymore.

I was driving home now—but was the word "home" really appropriate? A home is a place where you live with your wife and kids, everyone you love and work for, and find love and peace—a place to rest from the grueling challenges you face every day. Home was a place where I thought Karin, Philipp and Umberto waited for me, eager for my presence, for my strength.

But now this picture of "home" seemed amazingly distorted. It was more like I was going to war or to hell, a place ravaged by Walter, Karin and their lies. I wanted to stop the car and go build a fire and sleep on a beach by the Bay rather than face my son with what I now felt for his mother. But I couldn't do that. Instead I had to deal with this situation and try to preserve whatever sense of stability and security for him I could. If I could just find a way to take a momentary break from this madness and clear my head, maybe I could figure out what to do.

I let Karin out of the car in the parking lot. Both of us were silent. Parking the car, I headed out for my yacht knowing that talk was impossible right now. I needed to be alone. The unexpected events had kept us from having our "romantic" dinner; yet the hunger experienced earlier had disappeared into my nightmare world of depression and loss.

Stepping onto the welcome deck of my yacht, the only place in which I could now remotely call "home," I headed downstairs to rummage for something to drink, something hard but soothing. A half bottle of cognac and a nice full bottle of Jack Daniels beckoned to me. Grabbing the Jack Daniels and dropping a Coke into a bucket of ice, I climbed back upstairs to the aft deck. Pouring the whisky into a glass with a little ice, half of it disappeared in one sip, warming me immediately. I added a little more ice and a sip of Coke and gulped down the rest of the glass. I filled a new glass half full of whisky and half full of Coke and then looked around me.

I HAD LOST MY ENTIRE FORTUNE—MY HOTEL, MY BEVERLY HILLS CLUB AND THREE MILLION DOLLARS—TO A CROOK, AS WELL AS MY ENTIRE FAMILY.

Everything around me was still beautiful, but it was distorted— beautiful externally, but dark and lifeless, as if the landscape itself had lost its inner meaning. It was like having a beautiful, rare painting in your bedroom whose majestic lines and exquisite colors had enraptured you every morning when you gazed at it.

Then one morning, upon awakening, it still has the same colors and lines, but it has no impact and you turn away, puzzled and disappointed.

I felt like the lifeless landscape, empty and exhausted. Hopefully this was an illusion, like those I had seen in the Café de Paris. Yesterday, I had the feeling my life was like a delicate crystal globe, full of sparkle and life. But now some stranger had grabbed it out of my hands and smashed it on the ground. Now my life was splintered into ten thousand pieces, and none of the King's soldiers could put it together anymore.

There was a price on my head, an Austrian arrest warrant that deprived me of my homeland. I had lost my entire fortune—my hotel, my Beverly Hills Club and three million dollars—to a crook, as well as Karin and Philipp and my apartment in Monaco, even my good buddy, my little shadow, Umberto. *Monday, Monday*— you weren't good to me at all.

Being drunk and dwelling on the loss of your life and family is not a very productive pastime. The drunker I got, the more terrible it all seemed.

What more could I lose besides my life? And if that had any value, perhaps someone would have taken that away as well. I wondered how much more pain a human being could take. I sat on my aft deck, staring straight out to the sea until I couldn't think anymore.

I was finally burned out. Tilt! I had never felt anything like this before. It was a place far beyond any emotional pain I thought was possible. It was a new kingdom of pain, and it was ruled by an unyielding darkness.

I don't know how much more whisky I drank before I began to cry. It started with a few stray drunken tears and then became an unstoppable torrent. I felt my insides breaking into a thousand pieces—like that crystal globe—except this wasn't my external life. It was my own kingdom, what seemed like the essence of my soul boiling over into an ocean of pain and sorrow—a momentary breakdown of my mind and spirit.

During these moments of searing pain, I kept calling out to an unknown God: *What is happening to me? Why is this happening?* The now bleak and muted landscape, bereft of all meaning and beauty, as lifeless as the star-studded, silent sky, returned not even a faint echo of my anguish.

WHAT WAS THE NEXT STEP?
WHAT SHOULD I DO?

CHAPTER

24

Taking Stock

"Holy shit, what's happened to you?"

Tired of chanting a thousand questions to the emptiness that enveloped me, I fell asleep on the aft deck with a drained brown whisky bottle clutched tightly in a hand that shook slightly even as I slept.

When I woke up, miraculously I was somewhat myself, not that mad, sobbing lost soul of the night before. I was actually thinking and feeling almost normally—that is, normally for a caged wolf in an unfamiliar cell, but still with some intelligence and some real thought of survival, who had somehow managed to make it whole through that deplorable drunken night.

I knew that something had happened the night before that had come close to destroying my very essence. When I first woke up, I thought it might have been just a nightmare, but then, in the blinding sun, I saw the empty bottle of Jack Daniels and recalled with crystalline certainty my endless litany of questions and the final moments of emotional darkness before I blacked out.

What was the next step? What should I do? The only thing that was left was Gerhard, my only sure friend and the only person I knew whose wisdom I could still count on. Bypassing a shower, I walked like a wretched zombie to Gerhard's café. Unshaved, unshowered and wearing the same tear-soaked shirt that I had worn the night before on my "romantic" trek to Eze, a worn-out garment baptized by Karin's despair and mine, by my frustration and anguish. The tears may have been engendered by a different variety of pain, but they were just the same: wet, grimy and ever-flowing with the anguish of fear.

In a trance, I arrived in Gerhard's Café a quarter of an hour later looking like a deranged hobo. Angelique was astonished at my appearance. She had seen me dozens of times with bad hangovers, but never one that made me look like a putrefied phantom of my former self. To her credit, shocked and saddened as she was, Angelique still straightaway came up to me and hugged me, like any good mother would do for her beaten and forlorn child coming back from a fight in the school playground. I was saddened, bloody and bowed—a sorry sight, to be sure.

I sank in a chair and asked, "Is Gerhard around?" Before I could say anything more, Gerhard appeared suddenly from the kitchen, saying, "Holy shit, what's happened to you? Did you get run over by a train?"

I ordered nothing, but without any prompting Angelique brought me a double espresso, a Perrier and, as a bonus, a few potent headache pills. They both sat down and stared and me, waiting quietly for me to tell them what the hell was going on. I told them the whole story, and I swear, at the end, both had tears in their eyes and didn't know what to say.

FAR AWAY, AS IF THROUGH A LONG DARK TUNNEL, I HEARD GERHARD SAY, "SHIT!"

Angelique finally stood up, walked over to me and, while I was still sitting, took my head with both arms and pressed it onto her stomach and started to pet my hair. I heard her heart beating. Her body was warm and cozy, and I remember wishing I could sit there for a couple of hours. For a moment, a brief moment, I felt safe and comfortable.

She said nothing. I guess nobody knew what to say, although they could both imagine what I was feeling. I started to cry again, but Angelique never stopped petting my hair. Far away, as if through a long dark tunnel, I heard Gerhard say, "Shit!"

I don't know how long Angelique and I were fused together in that bizarre position, but suddenly I heard Gerhard say, "Come on, you're going with me to my apartment." Gerhard had a nice 1,200 square-foot apartment on the tenth floor of a high-rise over at Cap d'Ail, next to the Jardin Exotique Panorama. It had a balcony with a perfect view of the sea. Gerhard's girlfriend, Mireille, was a real Monagasque, so the apartments in her building were supported by the government. This was an apartment that would normally cost at least $4,500 monthly, but they only paid $600 monthly.

Mireille was a beautiful lady from southern France, ten years older than Gerard but with a perfect body, blond hair, big green eyes and perfect lips. She was popular with everyone for her cheerful disposition and sense of humor. Speaking fluent Italian, French and English, Mireille was a party animal. Because of her disposition, it was not possible to be sad next to her. If she thought you were the slightest bit off track, she would not quit until you began to laugh and couldn't stop. Many times I had thought how lucky Gerhard was to have her, how perfectly they fit together and how much fun it was to be with them. Mireille's Mom was already 94-years-old but still had her own business and, like her daughter, a conspicuously happy disposition.

In fifteen minutes we arrived at his apartment. Mireille was at work at the kindergarten, where she worked as a teacher. It was still morning, so she probably wouldn't be back until 5:00 p.m. Gerhard invited me to sit down in the living room, retrieved some coffee from the kitchen and looked at me intently. "Look, Hans, you can stay as long as you like here in my apartment, but you should really get over to America as fast as possible. I know you don't like to leave Philipp here, but if you're honest with yourself, what else can you do? At least you have a place to go and an opportunity. As you know, when you start making money again, you'll get back a lot of your power."

I sighed. "I guess I'll have to sell my yacht. Can you help?"

"I helped you buy it. I'm sure I can help you sell it. If I recall, you got it for $350,000 three years ago, so maybe I can sell it for $200,000 right away."

I nodded. *I loved that yacht,* I thought. *But what the hell?*

"That's a start," he continued. "If you stay here, I'm afraid you'll beat up Karin—or, if Walter is dumb enough to come to visit her, I'm sure you will kill him. I would hate to see you wind up in jail because of that stupid bastard."

"I'm sorry, but—"

"Don't apologize. Who wouldn't be angry in your situation? I would, especially with a child—and losing so much. But let's at

least try to get you out of here in one
piece. So please, stay in our guest
room—or on your yacht until we sell
it—but don't go to your apartment
anymore."

> "THINK ABOUT PHILIPP!
> YOU'RE A FIGHTER."

"I have a few things there," I said tensely, knowing that if I had
wanted some wisdom—and some hope of personal survival—I
had come to the right place.

"Well, get your shit out of your apartment now—avoid Karin
as much as possible and don't let her provoke you into destroying
your life with one impulsive action. Think about yourself and
think about your son. Nothing else. Please."

"Most of my personal items are back in Austria," I said. "All I
have here is two pairs of shoes, a couple of jackets and some
pants." I thought about my thirty handmade suits, my custom-
made shirts and shoes, my diamond rings, gold chains and other
jewelry. Back there I had acquired the finest clothes, paintings,
and antiques I could afford. "I am really fucked. I lost everything,
I mean everything!" I said.

"Yes, I know," he said ... and then began to echo my secret
thoughts, "but at least you're healthy and alive. I know that right
now that may mean nothing to you, but it's more than you think.
I could take you right now to a certain hospital I know—in fact
any hospital would do—and I promise you in a few minutes I
could find a dozen people who would change places with you in
a heartbeat." He looked at me seriously.

"Think about Philipp! You're a fighter. I've seen you in bad
situations before. All you need to do is make a decision to dig
yourself out of this hole and you will. You can't lose much else.

You now have a win-win situation—nothing to lose and everything to gain. Please, make a decent decision and get yourself on track."

"I know you're right," I said. "But first, I guess, I'll have to catch my breath."

Leaving Monaco

"I know you are running out of money ...."

After Gerhard made it clear that I had to decide on a course of action, he said, "Look, why don't you just lie here on the couch for about twenty minutes? Just relax. I'll call Roberto so he can work lunch with Angelique. Let me take you to Pulcinella. We can have some decent food, share a bottle of wine and consider the next steps."

I lay there while Gerhard bustled around in the other room, making some phone calls. For the first time in days, I stopped thinking about my problems. Instead, I thought about lunch.

It turned out that Pulcinella was a good choice for a planning session. Carlos, the owner, was an extremely nice, successful guy and had engineered a tiny cosmopolitan melting pot in the middle of one of the smallest countries in the world. Like most everywhere in Monaco, movie stars and sports celebrities mingled with the Mediterranean Jet Set and the local and international regulars. But no matter who they were, Carlos and his wife, Susan, were always welcoming. Good friends of Gerhard, my family and I were quite well-known there, and so was Umberto.

After a few minutes of relative peace, I suddenly felt sober again, my problems flooding over me like restless shades that will no longer be held at bay by the sunlight of optimism—even something as modest as anticipation of a pleasant lunch. I sat up stiffly and started to brood again.

Gerhard came in and sensed my mood immediately, "Good God, stop thinking about it! Here, let me pour you a shot of whisky. then take a quick shower." I sat there, still submerged in the thoughts that had overtaken me. "What do you want to do, Hans? Sit here the whole day and feel sorry for yourself?" I took the drink and smiled slightly. "Only by starting to live again and moving your life forward can you make things change. Come on, take your shower and let's go eat. I'm hungry as hell, aren't you?"

He pushed me in the direction of the bathroom, deviating momentarily to dart into his bedroom. When he came out, he handed me a pair of shorts and a nice shirt that he pressed into my hands. I thanked him and marched into the bathroom. I was there about ten minutes, soaping up under the soothing hot water, when Gerhard started banging on the door. I don't think he wanted me to stay anywhere alone for too long.

Finally I emerged. "Wow, you're looking better now, like a human being again and not a ghost!" When he said that, for a moment, the image of the pallid white face of Karin, groveling at my feet, flashed through my mind. Sensing a new negative mood, Gerhard looked at me and frowned, shaking his finger, and again pushed me slightly, this time in the direction of the front door.

Pulcinella was located on the Rue du Portier, five minutes away from the casino and fifteen minutes from Gerhard's apartment. On the way over Gerhard called in a reservation, an absolute necessity even for a friend of the owners. Even if you had reservations, there were times when that meant that Carlos put a little table in the kitchen for you. Not this time, though—Gerhard and I didn't want to talk about this in the kitchen.

We were lucky with parking. Five minutes later we entered the restaurant. Carlos spotted us as we came in, proclaiming loudly as he headed towards us, "Bon Giorno, Gerhard and Hansi!" Several of his customers stared as he said brightly, "Finally I see you again. Where the hell have you been? Do you want me to go broke? You know you're not allowed to stay away so long."

I looked at Gerhard, "Look at what we've done."

Gerhard nodded, "I know it. I feel guilty already."

Carlos came closer, hugged us and took us to our table on the terrace. It was a warm, beautiful day and we had lots of privacy. Like Gerhard's Mireille, Carlos' good humor was contagious. He could brighten a room just by walking into it. Yes, the food at Pulcinella's was excellent and the restaurant's décor was simple and cozy, but it was Carlos who made it happen.

As we sat on the open terrace, Gerhard ordered a bottle of Beaujolais Nouveau and a bottle of San Pellegrino to go with lunch. Carlos, ignoring a room full of customers, kept chatting with us, until his cheerfulness and kindness began to energize me again and I started slurping my minestrone with gusto, already in a better mood.

I dived into the spaghetti with the same gusto. Despite my misery, I couldn't help smiling—and Gerhard smiled back, happy to see that my darkness could still be chased away. I thought of one of Mom's powerful little aphorisms: "Though every door seems closed and you cannot find a way out, God can always open a little window." I breathed deeply. Gerhard was my window, and what happened next proved it.

He took a sip of wine, looked intently at me and said, "Listen, I know you're running out of money. I'll tell you what—I'll give you $5,000 in cash to buy a ticket to Houston, where your friend Manfred lives."

Despite his kindness, I frowned. But then, as though he could read my thoughts, he added, "I know. I know. I promise you I'll look after Philipp's interest. I'll watch over him like a hawk and call you immediately if anything seems wrong."

> "YOU WOULDN'T LIKE WATCHING THEM PLAY OUT THEIR SMELLY LITTLE GAME WITH YOUR SON IN THE MIDDLE."

I sighed audibly and smiled. "Yes, that's my biggest worry."

"Now let's tackle some of your other worries. For immediate cash, there's the yacht. Is there any impediment to selling it?"

"It's fully paid for, ready to sell."

"And your Bentley and the Range Rover?"

"The Bentley is paid in full, but the Range Rover is leased in Austria in Karin's name."

Now it was Gerhard's turn to sigh. We were both relieved. This wasn't going to be too difficult. "Okay, then the cars aren't any problem. Just take the Ranger back and I'll focus on selling your yacht and the Bentley. Stay here for a week and we'll concentrate on having a great time together. I promise I'll stick with you as much as possible, to help you get your mind relaxed and energized for your next big adventure. It will be like the old days, when you came here for vacation. Today is Friday and next

Wednesday's your birthday. So we'll celebrate Wednesday, and on Friday you'll hop on a plane to Houston."

I looked down. Although I felt fear in the pit of my stomach and resented it a little that someone else was mapping out my fate, I saw sunshine pouring through Gerhard's little window, and I tried to absorb his plan without showing any consternation. However, he sensed the undercurrent.

"There's no getting away from it, Hansi. If you stay here—if you get a job or start a business here, or anything—you could end up in the middle of a total nightmare. You know I'd let you stay here and work with me, but Karin and maybe Walter would still be in your face. You wouldn't like watching them play out their smelly little game with your son in the middle."

He was right. Although relaxed now, there was a wolf inside me yearning for revenge, one that had no scruples and no sympathy. I didn't want my son to see that wolf. Of course the wolf was me, but I also knew that the wolf was the real enemy I had to deal with—worse than Karin, worse than Walter. It was quite remarkable, I thought, that Gerhard understood the wolf and could still care about me. "You're right," I said, "Quite right. But I still think I'd make a pretty good busboy ...."

"You probably would," Gerhard laughed, "but that isn't you anymore. We're no longer children who can live on nickels and dimes. When you get to America, you'll have a more sedate view of things. This isn't the first time you've been broke or gotten a divorce.

"In the U.S., everything is possible. Look at Schwarzenegger. You told me how his uncle tried to get him a job as swimming instructor and a security guard in a public pool in Graz—how hard that was. In Austria people laughed at him for his silly bodybuilding obsessions. What's the difference between him and you? Only the quality of believing. He has it now and you will rise up to it again."

"You have more faith in me than I do," I said.

"You're probably right about that, at least for right now. All you have to do now is stay cool, relaxed. I know this is a tough one, but I want you to be nice to Karin."

"Nice to Karin ...?" I felt the wolf beginning to stir. "I think her comeuppance is long overdue."

"What does that mean, Hans? Clear your head for Christ's sake!"

"How can I just ignore—?"

Gerhard pounded on the table. A wine glass shattered on the floor. He ignored it. He stared in my face and said loudly, "Because she has your son; you don't!"

I took a breath, happy that the terrace was empty. The waiter came with dessert and mopped up the wine glass without comment.

"She is the mother of your child, and you don't want to do anything—I repeat, *anything*—to undermine her relationship with Philipp. No matter how much you hate her and Walter, they are going to be, at least for now, the only security he has. And believe me, his father's sudden disappearance is going to require a lot of explaining. So stuff all your hate and revenge in the closet and get down to the real task. You've got to rebuild your life."

Gerhard's formula was very difficult to swallow, although there was a little voice in me that agreed already. Philipp could not possibly understand what had happened between Karin and me, and despite what I thought of her, Karin loved Philipp with at least some beneficent variety of an irreplaceable mother's love.

For the moment, Karin was Philipp's connection with the very stuff of life: food, clothing, toys, candy, whatever he needed, whatever he wanted, he had to look to her for it. Yes, his mother spoiled him and we argued about it, but it would be simply unconscionable to tear his main connection to reality from him. The fact was that Karin was still the key to my son's heart. Dealing with her properly with Phillip in mind would be my greatest challenge.

We left Pulcinella mid-afternoon, promising Carlos we would come back as soon as possible, of course. We drove back to Fontvieille, where Gerhard had to get back to work. It was, after all, a busy Friday afternoon. Hugging him goodbye, I headed in the direction of my yacht. Once there I went to my bar, took out a snifter and poured a cognac, then went up to my aft deck to make one of the hardest calls of my life.

Family Decisions

*Every sin that I had ever committed was being paid
for in a few weeks.*

"Hansi, Hansi, is that you?" my mother said anxiously when
she heard my voice.

"Yes, Mamma, it's me. How's everything going?" I spoke
loudly and quite slowly, knowing that she was hard of hearing.

She said, "I'm okay, but your brother brought me the newspaper. What's happening to *you*?"

I thought, *Here we go again.* Couldn't Franz have had the
common sense and decency to call me before he said anything to
her and paraded my alleged crimes before her in the local newspaper? I knew I had to say things with clarity and self-confidence.

"Mom, you know our town, always looking for something
to gossip about. Believe me, it's not as bad as whatever that old
rag says."

Avoiding all technicalities, like my deal with Linkov, I tried to explain how some unscrupulous people had created unforeseen problems for me. Whatever words I said, I was somehow transmitting my somewhat spurious message of safety, all the while realizing that no matter what she said, she was transmitting a true message of love and trust to me. The purity of her love filled my eyes with tears, but I knew it wouldn't do anyone any good to break down and sob on the phone.

It was even harder when she added, "Your Father was asking for you. He often wakes up in the middle of the night and calls out your name."

I thought of my father, paralyzed in his bed wearing Pampers, crying for me, and I couldn't see him, say anything that could comfort him, or provide for him in these critical years. What a piece of shit I really was! Tears flowed down my face, even as I made every effort to keep my mother from knowing. At times I was shaking so violently that I had to take a big sip of Cognac to keep from going to pieces.

I totally lost it when she said, "How is Philipp doing? Is he okay?" The conversation had to end. I said, "Yes, of course, Mama. I'm going to get back to you soon—but I have an appointment now. Is that all right?"

"Take care, Hansi. I love you."

"I love you too, Mama." I sent her a kiss through the phone and said, "Give Dad a kiss from me."

As I sat on the sofa, partially covering the phone so she couldn't hear my sobbing, her last words were "Kiss Philipp for me. I love you both." Then she hung up.

I would like to say that my suffering for the day ended then and there, but I'm afraid I had another painful effort in front of me. If I wanted to see my son before I left for America—and I wanted to see him as much as possible—I would absolutely have to deal with Karin. What a fucking nightmare, I thought. Every sin that I had ever committed was being paid for in a few weeks. I am ready for heaven, I said to myself. But I knew I was lying. I wanted to live, and I had committed a lot of sins.

Like a prizefighter waiting for the next round, I prepared myself. I did breathing exercises that I had, then some push-ups and sit-ups, a few minutes of shadow boxing and some ju-jitsu moves, knowing I needed to be ready and confident for the next hurdle. If I had had a heavy bag, I would have banged the hell out of it.

This was like the eighth round of a 12-round match. Who were the spectators? Almost every damn person I ever met, the whole town of Wiener Neustadt and a lot of bureaucrats in the Austrian tax agencies. *Maybe you're going to stumble, maybe even fall, but come hell or high water, I told myself, you are going to make it through the next round. No matter what your body tells you, no matter how it urges you to give up, your brain and heart are stronger. You will prevail.*

After these brief invigorating moments of preparation, I took a quick shower and dialed Karin. When she picked up I said, "Listen, I want to make this as short as possible. I'm going to leave Monaco next Friday and I absolutely promise not to fight with you as long as you don't stand in my way with Philipp. You made your choice and that's it, as far as I'm concerned. I don't want to talk about that for one more second." I stopped for a moment and listened to silence. Finally, I said, "Are you there?"

"I'm listening," she replied.

"Okay, I just wanted to make sure you were there. So, now, this is what I want. Are you listening?"

"I told you I was."

"In the next few days, I want to spend as much time as possible with Philipp. Please bring him over to Gerhard's Café, along with Umberto, so he can spend time with me on my yacht until we leave."

"I have no problem with that."

"Before I leave, we have to talk. I need to know what your plans are and where Philipp will grow up."

"I'll tell you what I know."

"Another thing—and this is critical. Tell Walter that as long as I'm still here—and it's only a week—it would not be that good for his health if he visited Monaco, anywhere in Monaco."

"I'm sure that you won't have to worry about that."

"Thank you."

I paused, thinking now about my limited resources. "I'm going to get over to the bank here and will give you $2,000 so that you have enough money to make the transition to whenever he does arrive. As you probably know, I have hardly any money for my trip, so you'll be mostly on your own after that."

"Okay, Hans," she said in a restrained voice that had dropped below the freezing point. "I'll be at the café in two hours."

The last round had gone all right, and I was still in the ring.

A Birthday Party Arranged

*... with all her dazzling display, she no longer had
any physical attraction for me.*

When I got to Gerhard's, it was really crowded and people
were pushing just to get in. I decided to cross the street and sit
on the concrete sea wall and watch the tourists until Karin and
Company arrived. Finally she appeared. Philipp was wearing a
Spiderman backpack, and when he saw me he ran as fast as his
little legs could carry him, jumping into my arms with the pure
abandon of a small child.

As he kissed and hugged me, Umberto was jumping up and
down, frantic with his own happiness, wagging his tail and
barking. That was my last truly happy moment for quite some
time.

I knew that it might be—and with the will of my iron
prizefighter persona I tried not to think of the future or let the
absolute pleasure of being with my child overwhelm me. I looked

at Karin placidly, with little emotion. I said, "Thanks," trying not to look in her eyes.

When had we made love for the last time? It was only a couple of days ago, but it seemed like a month. Unbelievable. A time when I thought she stood loyally with me against the tide of events that were coming down on us.

I took Philipp's stuff from her. Although I tried to rest my eyes elsewhere, how could I help but notice how impeccably dressed she was? She was wearing a short red skirt, a blouse with a plunging neckline, everything tied tightly together so that you could see exactly the contours of the body I had so much admired and loved. To me she was still sexy and beautiful, but cold and rapacious, dressed for a night of succulent pleasure, her only real concern being to find the right full-blooded victim for an evening's dalliance. But actually, Karin had already chosen her next victim.

Would it be better for me to imagine them being happy and prospering together rather than dwelling on my comfort at the image of her feasting on that poor idiot as just another satisfying meal? I chose neither. Instead, I chose to put all that out of my mind. The fact was, with all her dazzling display, she no longer had any physical attraction for me. I simply could not be impressed. The wound was way too deep. In a strange way, I started to feel sorry for her. *What on earth is wrong with me?* I thought. *I should be sorry for myself.* Yet in a way, it made sense. I had escaped from her, but she had to live with herself. I think I preferred the former.

I left her and walked to the yacht with my two buddies. Philipp was talking and talking and asking and asking. We took all his stuff to the yacht, and after a few entreaties that didn't fall on deaf ears, I agreed to take Philipp to McDonald's.

The three of us, Philipp, myself and Umberto, had a great dinner a la McDonald's—not my favorite dining spot in Monaco, but where else could you get a weird little plastic toy "for free" or win ten million dollars by drinking a Coke? It was a very relaxing evening, and after McDonald's we went back to the yacht and watched a kid's movie, quietly enjoying ourselves.

The next couple of days we developed a regular routine, a routine I would remember and long for far into the years to come. First we would go to Gerhard's, then to the park, then swimming on the beach and a walk back on the path from La Mala. It was such a bittersweet pleasure to watch Philipp play with Umberto, climbing up the rocks to poke around in the caves, chasing squirrels and birds with abandon and throwing stones into the sea's white foam.

FROM TIME TO TIME I TRIED TO INHALE DEEPLY, WANTING TO REMEMBER THESE LAST MOMENTS TOGETHER.

By the time we reached home, my pockets were crammed with seashells, odd little pieces of driftwood, and once in a while an old coin or two. That's what happens when you hang out with a sweet little kid and a frisky little dog.

As we did these things, I thought how easy and beautiful life could be. We didn't need expensive restaurants, designer clothes, diamond-studded cufflinks or million-dollar haircuts. All the glamour and charisma of Monaco with its gluttonous appetite for wealth, celebrity and power was easily eclipsed by the subdued but staggering grandeur of its natural treasures of sea, sand and stunning mountains.

I knew that somehow our love for each other would endure beyond these moments, but soon circumstances still unknown to my son would change his life forever. From time to time I tried to inhale deeply, wanting to remember these last moments together. Why? Because this was the real value of life. And I wanted to imprint it in my heart and mind forever.

I called Karin every day and told her that everything was okay. I made it a daily part of my call to let Philipp speak with her alone. In those moments, even when I went into another cabin, it seemed that a deadly silence began to fill the yacht. I was still hurt, but the brutal hate that had seized me before was gone. Somehow, I think, my love for my son assuaged it as I slowly recognized that without her, I would certainly not have him. And he was without a doubt the greatest gift of my life.

It was Wednesday. I groggily looked out of my cabin to see bunches of blue and red balloons floating around the yacht. When I went outside, the whole yacht was crowded with balloons, some tied to the railing, others held by little Teddy bears squatting in corners with heart-shaped balloons, still others blocking the stairwells and flooding the deck. Making my way to the aft deck, I found a table with a huge cake inscribed "We love you, Hansi— Happy Birthday!" Sitting nearby was a wine lover's fantasy, a bottle of Veuve Cliquot with a bottle of orange juice, undoubtedly meant for my son. I could only guess who had done this, but the only suspect was Gerhard.

I couldn't dream of Karin wasting her time on something so trivial now—trivial from her point of view, perhaps, but from my point of view, having a real birthday was life-changing. To make matters even better, Philipp soon awoke and stumbled out in his little Spidey pajamas. "Good morning, Daddy," he said and gave me a kiss.

I said, "Good morning, Prince Sunshine! Are you okay?"

"Yes, but Daddy, I don't understand. It's not my birthday again, is it?"

"No, not yours."

"Mmmmm," he said. "Not Umberto's." Then, looking over at the table he said, "He doesn't like cake!" He looked around. "I'll bet it's *your* birthday, Daddy!"

"Why, you could be right!"

"Who brought all the balloons?"

"I'm not sure …."

"It's probably Gerhard. He buys a lot of stuff for us, doesn't he?"

It was a sobering thought. Even Philipp had noticed my friend's generosity. But he probably didn't know that when your life is falling apart, like mine was, the importance of these little favors—and some really big ones—were magnified a thousand times. "You're right. It must have been Gerhard. Later today you'll be able to sing Daddy 'Happy Birthday' and blow out the candles for me. Then you can borrow a wish from me, and from what I've heard, it will surely come true." When Philipp heard that his wish might come true, he got very excited and began to smile.

For that reason, we brought the cake with us when we went to Gerhard's for breakfast. Gerhard hugged me and Angelique embraced me warmly, pressed herself against me and planted a kiss firmly on my mouth. The love and heat she put into it made my day—and it was still early! Angelique was very pretty, but she had a boyfriend, and the last thing I wanted to do was fall in love with her and risk destroying someone else's romance. And after all, I was about to leave in a couple of days. But I did love that kiss and the feeling that somebody else cared for me.

Philly and I had a great birthday breakfast together. Philly watched me light the candle and got to make his wish. After that we sang "Happy Birthday" together. A moment later, Gerhard strolled out and said, "Your party is at 5:00 tonight, my friend. I've invited a lot of my customers, so you better be on time."

"No, you're crazy," I said, startled by this new expression of his generosity. "I wasn't expecting—"

He ignored me. "I called Karin and she'll take Philipp for tonight," he said, smiling. "I suspect it's going to be a very long party."

"You've spent far too much money on me already. I can't accept any more of this," I protested.

Giving me his fiercest mock reproachful look, Gerhard said, "You know what, Hansi? Shut up and enjoy your birthday and the great future that's waiting for you in America. Besides, I sometimes have to do something for my regulars, and this is a great opportunity because everyone knows you and likes you." He smirked. "In other words, you're giving me a grand occasion to bond with my customers. Who knows how much money I'll make because of this party?"

"Bullshit!" I said softly and smiled. "Okay, thanks," I said, vowing to myself to restrain from any further negative comments. Very soon, I would be unhappily out of his orbit, and this would be a wonderful way to say farewell to Monaco.

After a pleasant afternoon of swimming and playing on the yacht, I brought Philly home. Karin greeted me at the door with a cursory "Happy Birthday."

CHAPTER

28

A Farewell Present

I will never, ever forget that night on my yacht under a
star-filled Monaco sky on my 43rd birthday.

I bent down and gave Philly a kiss, petted Umberto, turned around
and left. As I made my way back to the yacht, I thought how
unbelievable it was that just a couple of days ago we were telling
each other how much we were in love and having what I thought
was completely satisfying sex, and now we were treating each
other like nothing like that had ever happened. We had become
complete strangers.

I arrived at the yacht around 3:45 p.m. and took a nap, setting
my alarm to ensure I'd make it to my own party on time. I fell
asleep immediately. Within minutes after the alarm went off,
looking forward to the evening and friends, I was on my way
to Gerhard's.

Arriving, the place was already overflowing with regulars. I
relaxed as it was quickly apparent that everyone was in fine spirits.

I don't think anyone missed an opportunity to hug and kiss me and wish me a "Happy Birthday." Angelique kissed me the way she had in the morning, and once more, the warmth of that kiss made me feel like a million dollars.

Fortunately, I was not drunk at the time, because if I had been, my reaction might have been a bit more dramatic, and perhaps quite stupid. And stupid was not what I wanted to be, not during my last days in Monaco.

Mireille, Gerhard's fiancé, came up to me and kissed me, wishing me a "Happy Birthday." She knew the whole story about Karin and me and at one point she put her head on my shoulder and whispered in my ear, "Don't be worried, darling. Everything will be okay. We both love you and Philipp very much. Don't worry." She kissed me again and again.

As the evening wore on, I was more intoxicated from love than from alcohol. All kinds of wonderful ladies showered me with kisses; guys who were perfect strangers to me hugged me affectionately and extended birthday wishes. There was, of course, lots of drinking, continual music and dancing, and as high a level of spirits as I had ever seen in any Monaco club.

By the time Mireille came up to me and introduced me to Rosa, I had begun to forget all my troubles, and they completely vanished when this black-haired Spanish beauty invited me to the middle of dance floor. She was around thirty-years-old with a perfectly contoured figure, and her dark brown eyes shone brightly through her designer glasses. Her demeanor remained distant as we glided over the dance floor, despite her dramatic, sexy execution of rumba and foxtrot steps.

But as I watched her dance, with her perfect hourglass body, wide hips and dazzling décolletage, I felt I was being drawn into the cave of a luminous Earth goddess, glowing with inviting, honey-like sensuality in the middle of this perfect night.

In the middle of a dance, Mireille actually interrupted us and asked me to dance, as Rosa stood aside compliantly. Mireille told me that Rosa had come here with her parents from Spain, and whispered, "She has pretty much the same problems as you, if not worse. Her husband decided to screw around with her 21-year-old sister, decimating a five-year marriage."

All I could say to that was, "Shit, poor girl."

When I went back to dance with Rosa, it was almost as if I could penetrate her mind and heart and see behind the walls she had erected around herself. She was a beautiful woman with a broken heart like mine, trying to fake normality and conviviality in a setting where no romantic drama could ease her heartbreak or sense of betrayal.

As the party went on and on, I tried to make conversation with her, but I had no Spanish and she didn't speak German. We were linked only by our shared English, which was very poor. We were still hanging out at 11:00 that evening, and since everyone had already hugged and kissed me and wished me a thousand happy returns, my celebrity status was a bit diminished.

In my broken English, I asked her if we could go out for a while, sit down on the sea wall and watch the splendid full moon that had risen some hours before. We took our glasses with us, mine filled with whisky, hers with champagne, and gazed together at the splendid view of the castle on the top of the rock wall, blazing with lights under the full moon.

We sat there for several minutes in absolute silence until I felt her hand slowly pressing against mine. She turned toward me and took off her glasses. We gazed in each other's eyes. She gave me a gentle kiss on the cheek, and shortly after that our lips found each other in a never-ending kiss, and I began to pray that time would stop altogether.

It would have been wonderful to be able to speak fluently with each other. But all that could pass between us was a few imperfect exchanges in English and the synchronized, staccato beating, as we embraced, of two broken hearts. Our touching, our kissing was not really the union of a perfect love, for in fact we barely knew each other, and anything we did know was probably through Mireille.

No, our embraces were based on some desperate reaching out for emotional survival, seeking comfort and help from a stranger on this magical night.

This experience with Rosa was the capstone of a night filled with the love of perfect strangers, which nurtured and revived me in my desert of emotional desolation. If the birthday party revived my spirits, my encounter with Rosa renewed my hope for life and the potential of new love.

We knew, through Mireille, that our essential bond was a mutual experience of treachery and pain, and that the sudden deep feeling that had overtaken us for each other was based on a loss of comfort with life itself. Justified or not, our core identities began to drift and merge in an accelerating wave of kisses and embraces as the full moon watched.

Poets and seers have given the moon a life and consciousness of its own. Was it astonished at our audacity in seeking even temporary happiness with such sudden impetuosity while it spread its ancient light over the sea and castle? Did our frenzied entwining like two vines on this antique stone wall amuse the ancient guardian of the Earth, who has indifferently cast its pale brightness over all nighttime revels on Earth in every age of passion and romance?

Now, besides the crashing of the waves, there was an uninterrupted silence. We sat there, holding hands, until I asked her in my broken English, "You like to go—to my yacht?"

She looked into my eyes and said, "Si, mi amore." Although I could still hear the faraway music and murmuring of the happy crowd at Gerhard's, we were already in a different world. This world had its own balloons and birthday cake, but in a solemn, ceremonial sense—a place where human and divine love merged in a moment of celebration, where time collapsed in momentless time, where briefly we could breathe the air of eternity.

We stood up and walked along the pier, hand-in-hand. I could see my yacht in the far distance, framed by a grand panorama of stars, sea, moon and rock. It was like a scene from a movie, too beautiful and heart-touching to be true. That night two badly hurt souls, drawn like magnets to each other, found healing in a brutal and violent world where money ruled and love had lost all meaning.

Once more in silence, we arrived at my yacht. I poured the remainder of my cognac in a whisky glass, gave her a sip and took one for myself. And then something entirely new in my experience happened. Still completely speechless, we dropped our clothing on the deck and retreated to the master bedroom where, for one hour, we kissed, hugged and petted, consumed with each other, drowning in each other's naked being.

It was not like ordinary sex, but some extraordinary cataclysm of desperate clinging, of a physical search by someone in need of healing, of touching, of some physical evidence of warmth and love in this world.

That night we found it in each other, as the warmth of our bodies melted the coldness of our forsaken hearts. I don't know how long we entwined ourselves, sometimes touching, sometimes kissing and sometimes simply weeping silently with the grace and pleasure of the moment. The few words we spoke were simple as we kissed away the tears from one another's cheeks—nothing more than "amore" or "darling," or "baby," or "Oh God," till the grand finale of the evening.

I will never, ever forget that night on my yacht under a star-filled Monaco sky on my 43d birthday. We were tightly pressed against each other when we fell asleep, and we remained that way throughout the night. Perhaps we thought that if we let go we would lose each other and be lonely again. We were both exhausted but amazed that we could again experience a glimmer of happiness.

After this night we knew that our lives were not completely finished and that, whatever happened between us, life would once more take on a semblance of meaning. For me, and I imagine for her, the emotional healing process had begun.

Waking in the morning, the sun was already high in the sky. Strangely, I didn't have a hangover. When I saw Rosa lying very still in the sunlight, her perfect body almost glowing in the bright light of day, I felt compelled to gently brush her long hair with my fingers and softly kiss every inch of her until she opened her eyes suddenly, still languishing in my kisses.

THE PRIZEFIGHTER IN ME WAS NURTURED BY THAT EVENING.

"I thank you for last night, Rosa," I said.

"Si, mi amore. Very wonderful," she whispered back.

In most cases in my distant past such events as the night before triggered only one overwhelming thought in my mind, something like "Run, rabbit, run! Run as fast as you can!" Yes, I admit it now, at times like these I would grab my clothes and run to escape from the lovely pit of danger lying next to me.

It was completely different this morning. The love I felt for Rosa was overwhelming, but I knew that in a couple of days we would have to leave and never see each other again. One more time I tried to imprint the picture of me lying beside her in the photographic album I wanted to cherish and keep in my inner world. Although both of us in our lower natures could have looked for payback to our ex-lovers and exploiters in last night's escapade, I viewed it as a gift from the law of attraction rather than anything negative directed at others.

The prizefighter in me was nurtured by that evening. Down as I was, I now felt an urgent need to fight my opponents, known and unknown—and for that I must truly survive. It was hard to believe that only a couple of days ago I longed, even prayed, for an end to this horrid life on Earth. Now I was ready to fight not only for my son, but for myself, and the ability to enjoy life and happiness in a renewed and wonderful world.

At that moment, I actually folded my hands together and murmured, "Thank you, God; thank you so much for last night, and for this knowledge that I can still feel and believe in love. This has been the best birthday present in a long, long time."

I kissed Rosa goodbye, pressing my body against hers. She gave me a long, long intense kiss in return. As I basked momentarily in the comfortable warmth of her soft body, she spoke to me for the last time. "I never will forget you, mi amore," she said, then added, "Thank you and God bless you."

We got ready to leave, putting our clothes on slowly. Unsure of our future but content in the moment, we embraced each other and kissed again and again. We said goodbye as we left the pier going our separate ways. It was my *Casablanca* where Humphrey Bogart says goodbye to Ingrid Bergman for the last time ... a farewell to something wonderful and brief.

29

Gerhard's Sendoff

"Repay me by becoming a big success in America.
That will be more than enough."

I thought I should cry, but I couldn't. Whatever the outcome
of our relationship, I still felt happy and fulfilled, fundamentally
hopeful about the future. Despite everything, my troubles
seemed to be dissolving in the warmth of a fine Monaco morning.
I was in wonderment that I could still experience deep happiness,
even if it was momentary. Oh, my God! In the midst of all this,
my hope had been reborn.

I had one more day to spend with Philipp, but first I wanted
to call Gerhard. After I thanked him for the party, he asked,
"Where the hell were you? One moment you were there and then
you were gone!"

"I had something I had to do. It was important to me."

"I suppose I shouldn't ask."

"Not right now." I'm sure with Rosa missing from the party too it didn't take a master detective to surmise where I had been. "I don't know how I can ever repay you ...."

"Repay me by becoming a big success in America. That will be more than enough."

"Well, today is the last day with Philipp. Would you like to join us at the yacht for some fishing? After that you'll have plenty of time to recover from me."

"Don't be stupid," he said. "I'll miss you. But America's in the cards for you right now, and if I were you I'd get myself psychologically ready to make that transition. It's going to be a big one."

Gerhard did go fishing with us, arriving on the *Macau* shortly after Karin brought Philipp and Umberto. A couple of minutes later we headed out into the blue, shining sea, my last real glimpse of the Mediterranean before I left. We fished for a while, ending up in the Bay at La Mala, where we anchored and went swimming. The dinghy from the restaurant picked us up, as always, and we had a superb lunch. Gerhard continued to encourage me and I talked while Philipp and Umberto played in the sand.

When evening fell, Gerhard left to work the night shift at his café. Philly, Umberto and I stayed on my yacht, watching *The Wizard of Oz* and the first twenty minutes of *The Fellowship of the Ring*, and then went to bed. While the previous day had been quiet and pleasant, even now I have trouble thinking about my last day, and last night, in Monaco. Gerhard had already bought the ticket for a 4:00 p.m. non-stop to Houston, my new adventure. It wasn't easy to fall asleep that night, but after tossing around for several hours, I finally blacked out.

I woke up late, at 9:00 in the morning, and called Karin. I needed to take Philly home, pick up my few belongings, including my luggage, and give her some last minute information about the least entangled part of our financial affairs. This would be a fucked-up day that I had been trying so hard to avoid, but the reality was here.

Forcing myself to look at it as an adventure, I imagined I was a little Hobbit looking for a golden ring in a faraway land. And if I were a Hobbit, I suppose that Gerhard would be Gandalf. And Karin, well, I could only see her as the bad witch in *The Wizard of Oz*, although she looked a lot more like the good witch. I think you can always learn something from watching kids' movies. But I knew I wouldn't be watching any more for quite some time.

Philly woke up, we got all ready together, and then we were on the way to my apartment. I knocked on the door and Karin opened it, perfectly dressed as always, ready to leave in a split second for an exciting day without Hans to get in her way.

Philipp grabbed her around the legs, said, "Hi, Mommy! I had a great time with Daddy," and began to report on our last week together. Meanwhile I retreated to the bedroom to retrieve my two suits, two pairs of shoes, a couple of dress shirts and a couple of casual ones. *Wow! After all this work,* I thought, *this is all I have left?* When I returned to the living room, I asked Karin for the key to the Range Rover, where I was going to put my things to go to the airport.

"I'm going to Gerhard's now to work out a few things with him," I said. "After that I'll pick up some money for you, and on the way to the airport, I'll give you some last instructions. Then you can enjoy your new, carefree life." Surprisingly, she said nothing. There was nothing that she could possibly say that I wanted to hear or would be able to believe.

I gave Philly a hug and a kiss and said, "Okay, buddy, I'll be back pretty soon, and then you'll have to take me to the airport. I have to go somewhere for a while. When I come back, I'll have a present for you, but you have to be a good boy."

His little arm embraced my neck. He gave me a kiss and said, "Okay, but hurry up. I'll be waiting for you."

I left for my last meeting with Gerhard, knowing that the toughest moments were still ahead of me—those terrible goodbyes, first to Gerhard, then to Philipp and Umberto, whom I might never see again, and finally to Karin. Yes, by this time I had begun to tear away that layer of hatred and resentment I felt for her and Walter. Some kind of calmness had set in, and I could see past that dark veneer to the searing, impossible-to-accept reality that I still loved her.

That incredible truth did not prevent me from realizing that my marriage to her was finished forever, but there was a pain there that would burn in me for a long time—a pain of remorse and unrequited love that even hatred and anger could not cover up.

Before heading to the café, I went to the bank and picked up $2,000. My account was down to $8,000, positively a joke for anyone who lived in Monaco. I arrived at Gerhard's and found Angelique there too. I thought, *Oh, my God, this isn't going to make anything easier.* Gerhard came up to me immediately. "I'm very proud of you, Hansi," he said. "You're definitely doing the right thing."

A few minutes later, Angelique embraced me, kissing me on the left and right cheeks and then on my lips. "Hi, Cheri," she said with big tears in her eyes.

I cleared my throat and said, "Everything is fine, mon ami. Everything is fine."

We sat down together in a corner of the café. Moments later, before I actually ordered anything, Angelique placed a double espresso and a San Pellegrino on the table before me. When she left, I handed a thick envelope to Gerhard. It contained the paperwork for my Bentley, the title for my yacht, a handful of keys and a few other documents.

Gerhard took out its contents, looked at them carefully and then handed me his own envelope. "Here is $5,000 and here is your ticket. Please, don't say anything and take it. I don't expect it back, so please shut up. I don't want to cry here, so if you don't mind, we can talk another time, probably on the phone. I love you like my own brother, and I'll miss you."

He kept talking, but I couldn't hold my tears back anymore. As they streamed down my face, I put my sunglasses on. "Okay, I can't talk anymore either. I'll call you as soon as I get to Houston."

I stood up. Gerhard hugged me, and then Angelique ran over and put her arms around both of us. All three of us stood there with tears running down our faces. At this point, I started to tremble. All I could think of was, "Oh God, let me get out of here before I completely break down!"

I started to leave. I knew I could only say one more thing before I lost my voice completely. When I reached the door, I turned back and managed: "Bye, guys, I love you very much." I went outside and began to run as fast I could.

I ran and ran, even when I was almost completely out of breath, managing to make it to the end of the port. I stared around me at the gorgeous scenery, the clear sky and the castle on top of the steep rock wall. "WHY?" I asked. But there was only the silence of the sea and sun.

The last week was a roller-coaster of feelings—from thoughts of taking my life and preparing to die to fantastic moments of love and sharing with my friends. Perhaps, I thought, I don't

OH, MY GOD! IN THE MIDST OF ALL THIS, MY HOPE HAD BEEN REBORN.

deserve to live in such a beautiful, breathtaking place, a place most people will never see or experience in their lifetime.

Perhaps I never will live in such a place again, nor will I ever share another night of such intense romance with a beautiful woman as I did with Rosa, someone I will probably never see or hear from again. Yet when I looked at everything I had done, seen and experienced, I could only say, *But what a ride! What a fantastic ride!*

CHAPTER

30

Goodbye Dear Philipp,
Hello Houston

"No, you can't go. I want you here."

Finally reaching my yacht, I sat down on the pier. I needed to get strong again fast, for there was still one more horror to confront, the dismal reality of leaving my son behind with no idea when I would see him again. When I thought about it, I felt a darkness within myself, and a terrible nausea would begin to overtake me.

That last ride to the airport loomed as the greatest moment of terror in my life. I inconspicuously folded my hands and prayed, "Please, please, God, if You really exist, help me to get over this pain. If that is possible, let me arrive in Houston, but if not, let me die on the airplane. Please!"

I sat there for about twenty minutes, staring at my yacht for the last time and trying to prepare myself for the last act. Now it was time. As I headed out to the apartment, I realized again that

I had to make sure to give Philly the impression that everything was okay and that Daddy would be around the corner when he needed me. I knew that this was a great untruth, but also realized that I could not make him feel insecure, even though I myself did not know what was really ahead. Perhaps there was some rainbow out there for me.

I thought of Jesus carrying his cross on the road to Golgotha. I felt some kind of emotional solidarity with his journey, and with that terrible suffering in mind, my own pain seemed to subside somewhat. The image was terrible, but it restored some balance, some proportion to my thinking.

I called Karin and told her to bring Philipp and Umberto to the car. When I arrived she was already there, and we all took off to the airport. For the last time I took Basse Corniche along the coast, and the breathtaking view was as spectacular as when I first saw it. Truly, I had lived in Paradise!

On the way, I gave Karin an envelope and said, "Here's $2,000. It should be enough for you to make it through the next couple of weeks. I paid the rent for August already. Gerhard will take care of the yacht slip and the yacht."

She said, "What's with the yacht, anyway?"

"You don't need to worry about that," I said "It's being sold. As to Philipp, I'll take care of him. Have no doubts about that! Your lover will have to take care of you. You can understand that, can't you?"

She didn't reply. I added, "The only thing you need to do is return the Range Rover to the leasing company in Austria or pay the monthly payments. We can talk about it when I'm in Houston. You have the next five weeks to figure out what to do with it."

"Walter will come to Monaco and stay for a couple of weeks. Maybe he'll take over the apartment."

I was silent for a moment. After a while I said tensely, "We'll see." I tried to blot out my anger by focusing on the beautiful scenic route, all the while making small talk with Philipp. When we arrived at the airport, I found a parking space. Then I took my luggage in one hand and Philipp in the other and went to the counter to check in. When I had my ticket, I picked up my son and carried him to customs.

It was time to say goodbye. I went down on my knees, hugging and kissing Philipp and Umberto. I looked deeply in my son's eyes and said, "Listen very carefully. Daddy loves you very much. I have to go on a long business trip, but I'll call you every day. You'll tell me what's going on, okay?"

He looked at my suspiciously. "What do you mean long, Daddy? How long?"

"I don't know," I said, shaking my head. "I just don't know."

"Then I don't want you to go," he said firmly. "Don't go!"

I tried to divert him. "You're a big boy now. You have to take care of Umberto for me. Pinky promise?" He shook his head and refused to take my pinky. "Please don't make this harder than it has to be."

"I'm going to make it real hard," Philipp said, and stamped his feet. "You're going to stay!"

"No, I can't," I said firmly and looked at Karin. She shook her head as if she couldn't really think of what to do.

I went over to her and hugged her without a kiss, then made a move towards customs. "No, I won't let you leave," Philipp said and ran to me. Karin tried to hold him back, but he pulled away from her and grabbed my leg. "Stay here!"

"I can't," I said, noticing that some of the people in line were staring.

He started to cry, loudly, "No, you can't go. I want you here." Karin was trying to dislodge him from my leg, but he just yelled louder. I saw a security officer near the customs gate turn his head and start towards me. A wave of nausea and a sense of helplessness came over me. Slightly weeping myself now, I pulled Philipp off my legs and Karin put her arms under his, sweeping him up, even though he was kicking and screaming. Umberto, quite upset, began to run around him, barking furiously. Karin moved swiftly away as the airport official came up to me.

Before he could say anything, I said, "He doesn't want me to go."

"Is that your son?"

"Yes," I said, taking a deep breath and wondering if he could see that I had been crying.

RELUCTANTLY, I WALKED TOWARDS CUSTOMS.

"Well, Dad, it happens every day around here. Yesterday it took two of us to pry a kid loose from his mother who was leaving for Viet Nam. He'll be all right. He just needs to calm down. That was your wife, wasn't it?"

"Yes, yes," I said.

"Are you okay?"

"Yes," I tried to smile.

I looked back. They were almost out of sight now. Karin was still carrying him, but he had calmed down a bit, or so I thought. I turned back to the customs official and saw he was headed back to his post. I quickly looked for somewhere to sit and saw an empty bench near the customs checkout area. I sat there with my face in my hands, the tears cascading down like a waterfall.

A couple of minutes later, after I calmed down slightly, I stood up and went to a window. I could see Philipp walking next to Karin, heading towards the airport exit. I pressed my face against the windows, my nails scratching the glass as I again broke down, sobbing uncontrollably.

People walked past me, gawking at me. I sensed their presence, but I didn't care. I had tried to hold these moments back, but the hole in the dam was too big for my finger—and for my heart, my mind and my soul, for that matter. Nothing could stop this flood of changes coming over me.

Reluctantly, I walked towards customs. The officer I had spoken to before came up to me when I was being processed and quickly waved me through. I smiled at him and he gently nodded. I tried to find them in another window, but they had gone. Finally I heard my flight called and I lumbered in the direction of the gate. As soon as boarding started, I went quickly to my seat. I asked the lady sitting near the window if she would mind terribly if I changed places with her.

She didn't really seem to care for the change, but looking at me and sensing my desperation, I think she complied out of some sense of compassion. The lady looked to be more than nice and she was beautiful. A good companion on a long flight, but I barely looked at her, pressing my face against another pane of glass, hoping to catch a last glimpse of my boy.

Though he had disappeared, I kept my gaze fixed out the window as we flew over Monaco and the Cote d'Azure and the millions of lights along the coast.

A sea of lights signaling goodbye to this reluctant pilgrim setting out to a strange destination in the New World rolled out in front of me. As we rose up into the sky, the terrain disappeared under a dense bank of clouds.

I lay back in my seat, closed my eyes and braced myself for the future, whatever that would be.

Acknowledgments

First, to Tony Robbins. His CD series *Power Talk* inspired me with his interview with Frank Kern. Frank explained there how he became a self-made multi-millionaire by selling products on the Internet. Thank you, Frank—your interview helped me greatly.

Second, to my son, Philipp. We had just opened up a hand car wash and it had rained every day since the opening. I was depressed and afraid of losing my business almost before I had launched it. Philipp and I were listening to Tony's CD when he said to me, "Dad, you should write a book. With what you have accomplished in the past, you should write a book about your life. I promise you, you will eventually become a millionaire. You are amazing, you need to tell your story."

Write a book? Not so easy. When I came to America in 1997, I could not speak one word of English. I was born and raised in Vienna, Austria ... where I spoke fluent German, not English. Now, nine years later, I speak okay English, but my writing, well, it needs a little help—an understatement.

But I continued to listen to that CD again and again. And, to get rid of my bad weather syndrome from the start-up car wash and the fear of failing, I said to myself, *What the hell can I lose?* I talked to my wife, Megan, and told her my idea. I told her I would move to my yacht and would live there while writing my story. She looked at me with a look and comment I knew well: "Really ..." but she knew that when I made a decision and had a vision, nobody could stop me.

I followed the advice of Frank Kern and hired a ghost writer to translate my weird German English into an understandable American English. The ghost writer did a pretty good job but eventually we split up because we differed in our vision for the book. I then wrote, myself, during 2009, a total of 1700 pages to create the first draft.

Megan patiently waited during those months ... Thanks, Baby, for your patience, support and love for that one year while I was barely at home, living on my yacht, obsessing on writing my life story. When I was not on the yacht, I was working with my son in our car wash business and visiting home only occasionally.

It cost me a ton of money to get to that point where we settled on a concept, and now, five years later, with some tweaking and editing, my first book is finished.

Many things have happened in my life since finishing what is now my first book. My story is not finished—more books are to come—there's much more to my story after I arrived in America.

I called different publishers but there was no contract or offer I felt comfortable with. Then Megan called one day and told me that she found a website called "The Book Shepherd" with Judith Briles, and I contacted her immediately. It was my lucky day. I really can say, she was and is "The Good Book Shepherd"; she earned that title. I never had the feeling she took advantage of me as a total "Greenhorn." No—the opposite happened. She treated me like I was a professional writer, building a platform of trust with me. I also can say that she charged me more than fairly. Thanks, Judith.

Also, my thanks to Nick Zelinger who created my cover and interior—his openness to my ideas and his flexibility and expertise were much appreciated.

As you now know, writing is not my profession; I write only for these reasons: First, to put my thoughts about my past in order. Second, I think you, my reader, can learn from my story. And third, I don't want to die with a "Bucket list" that was never "emptied"—I believe in living life! When I move to the next level of life I will have nothing on my page of what I think I missed. I did it all! It contains every important point of a life: Love, Success, Failure, New Beginning and finally, the most important thing, *never, never quit dreaming.*

Walt Disney said, "As long you can dream it, you can achieve it." I've embraced that idea, and I live it.

As to my story, many names have been changed. I'm not out for revenge or to hurt anyone, just to tell my story. At the end of the day, I may have made myself look better and sometimes worse than I deserve, depending on the memory of my feelings at the time.

Often, when I look back, it seems I may have dramatized a part of the story; sometimes the facts were too hard to believe, myself. "I did all that?—I said that?—OMG!"

But believe me, the story truly tells my experience ... and my life.

Enjoy and God Bless,
Hans Sitter

P.S. Gerhard, know that you saved my life. I love you, and your place ("Gerhard's Café" in Fontvieille in Monaco—it exists still today; visit him) remain in my heart.

Karli, Siegie, Vick, Christa, Joe and all my old friends and employees, I love you and hope you are doing well. I will never forget you guys.

About the Author
Johann "Hans" Sitter

Meet Hans Sitter, a legendary serial entrepreneur who has established and worked in an amazing variety of industries during his decades-long, roller coaster of a career. Trained as a butcher in Austria, he quickly realized that his interests and skills were in quite different areas from "butchering."

He is now in his 60s and the driving force behind one of America's most successful German restaurants. His entrepreneurial spirit led him in his youth first to establish several auto-related businesses. His connections in that industry then led him in broadly different directions: opening game rooms, bars, night clubs, a car dealership and body shop, operating restaurants and flipping properties.

Inspired by the hit TV series, *Dallas*, he opened a gas station in Austria calling it *DALLAS DISCOUNT*. He dressed his employees as Cowboys and got the attention that most companies only dream of. Within a few years, moneys flowed; he prospered and moved his family to a permanent residence to Monaco, where they lived among the rich, super rich and famous.

He then sold all his gas stations and with the proceeds, built a Hotel and Fitness center and a Las Vegas style men's club called "Beverly Hills Club." He then decided to sell that enterprise with the idea of moving to the US and starting a business there. Unfortunately, the buyer landed in jail before completion of the sale and Hans lost the entire business, along with his savings, yacht and apartment in Monaco ... the $3,000,000 owed him ...

everything. On top of his financial losses, there was an arrest warrant issued in Austria for tax evasion, and his wife spurned him for losing everything, leaving him for one of his long time friends.

With her exit, he lost his family and the daily contact he cherished with his two-year-old son Philipp and their beloved Cavalier King Charles Spaniel, Umberto. His story didn't end there, however. He didn't quit ... he started over ... again.

A close and loyal friend in Monaco bought him an air ticket to Houston, TX, gave him $5,000 and begged him to leave, to follow his original plan and start over again in America.

Bidding good-bye to a life he loved, he arrived in Houston, Texas, in September of 1996 with a little cash, two pairs of jeans and shoes and a few shirts. The English language was unknown to him. He knew one person in the States and joined him in Houston. That person eventually introduced him to his future wife, Megan. Soon after, his young son Philipp came for a visit and stayed—stepmother Megan became Mom.

Together, they created *SCHMATZ—The best from Vienna ...* he was the cook, Megan, the waitress. Hans never quit; always dreaming big. An observer of all things, he watched everything around him. As his English and his understanding of business in America improved, he recognized the real estate boom happening in Houston, Learning to make 90 days options with a minimum down payment on properties, Hans became the new American Cowboy: he loved the thrill of the deal and began to flip real estate, then bought a ranch and bred Longhorns. He tried it all. Nothing could stop him ... he thought.

Then with one wrong decision, his financial pinnacle became a valley and he had to file for bankruptcy in 2005. At least, this time he didn't lose his family. Once again, Hans started over ... this time selling Himalayan Crystal Salt and building with his own hands a spa. Partnering with the friend, they bought a property and opened up a hand car wash. It worked, but he was bored and doubly frustrated when it rained, delaying the development of the business. Hans needed more.

He and his son, Philipp began listening to CDs created by Tony Robbins, particularly the Money Masters series with Robbins interviewing millionaire Frank Kern who shared making his first million using a ghost writer. The light bulb went off when Philipp said, "Dad you should write a book. Your life story is as good as that of Frank Kern, You could be a millionaire again." With that, Hans started to write and, with help, put it all together. *The Last Days in Monaco* is the result and is just the first—there are three more books coming!

That same year, they built a restaurant next to the car wash: *King's Biergarten and Restaurant*. Over three years, it has expanded to 75 employees and over 300 seats. And in that three year period, restaurant revenues grew from $800,000 to in excess of $3,000,000. It has been awarded the Best German Restaurant designation in 2012-2013-2014 by *GermanDeli.com* and is consistently recognized as a Top Ten Restaurant for Service in Houston. As multiple reviewers have stated, "It's a hidden gem in Pearland, Texas."

TODAY, Hans remains happily married to Megan and his key business partner is his son Philipp who is now the Director of Operations and Marketing of King's Biergarten & Restaurant. Texans frequently see him in commercials on TV and he and the restaurant are often profiled within the media.

In his 60s, if you asked Hans if he plans on retiring, you will get a big smile and the response, "My hobby and my life intend for me to continue to be an Entrepreneur. I still enjoy THE THRILL OF THE RIDE and retirement would be for me, the death penalty. It would be like forbidding me to breathe and who in the hell wants to stop breathing and be dead?"

From rags to riches to rags and back to riches, Johann "Hans" Sitter is the classic serial entrepreneur. Provocative, engaging, a visionary ... he's like a lightning rod in your presence.

KingsBiergarten.com
Facebook.com/KingsBiergarten